Is a camel a mammal?

LONDON, NEW YORK,
MELBOURNE, MUNICH, AND DELHI

DORLING KINDERSLEY
Project Editor Victoria Wiggins
Senior Designer Sheila Collins

Managing Editor Linda Esposito
Managing Art Editor Diane Peyton Jones

Category Publisher Laura Buller

Production Controller Sophie Argyris
Production Editor Rebekah Parsons-King

Jacket Editor Manisha Majithia
Jacket Designers Silke Spingies, Nim Kook

Publishing Director Jonathan Metcalf
Associate Publishing Director Liz Wheeler
Art Director Phil Ormerod

DORLING KINDERSLEY INDIA
Senior Art Editor Chhaya Sajwan
Art Editors Niyati Gosain, Shipra Jain,
Kanika Mittal, Payal Rosalind, Anuj Sharma,
Priyanka Singh, Shruti Soharia Singh,
Vidit Vashisht
Managing Art Editors Priyabrata Roy Chowdhury,
Arunesh Talapatra
Senior Editor Monica Saigal
Editors Gaurav Joshi, Archana Ramachandran,
Suparna Sengupta
Managing Editor Pakshalika Jayaprakash
DTP Designers Dheeraj Arora, Neeraj
Bhatia, Sourabh Challariya, Jagtar Singh,
Anita Yadav
DTP Manager Balwant Singh
Production Manager Pankaj Sharma
Picture Research Sakshi Saluja

First published in Great Britain in 2012
by Dorling Kindersley Limited
80 Strand, London WC2R 0RL

A Penguin Company

Copyright © 2012 Dorling Kindersley Limited

2 4 6 8 10 9 7 5 3 1
001—185367—02/07

A CIP catalogue record for this book is available from the British Library.
ISBN 978 1 4093 7645 3

Printed and bound by South China Printing Co. Ltd, China

See our complete catalogue at
www.dk.com

Is a camel a mammal?

Contributors: Kim Dennis-Bryan and John Woodward

Contents

Quiz number
Each quiz is numbered, so you can look up the relevant set of answers by quiz number.

13

A **spitting cobra's venom** can cause p...

1 In the animated film *Finding Nemo*, what was the shrimp called?

2 I am an orange fish with white stripes that lives in sea anemones. What am I?

3 What is a group of lions called?

4 In a food chain, which of these are decomposers?

5 On average, how many bees are there in a hive?

6 How many times its own height can a flea jump?

7 How many different species of shark do you think there are?

8 Which of the following is not an amphibian defence strategy?

9 What kind of bird was the extinct dodo?

10 How do f... where to fin...

11 Mammal... pouches in th...

Reference

Amphibians and reptiles
Although they look similar, amphibians and reptiles have very different lives. Amphibians such as frogs are thin-skinned animals that must stay damp, and they usually breed in water. Reptiles such as snakes have scaly skins that stop them from drying out, and many live in deserts.

Salamanders and newts
These long-tailed amphibians live in moist places, or in streams and ponds. Newts are more aquatic, and breed in water. Many salamanders do the same, migrating to ponds in the breeding season, but others lay eggs in damp ground. They are all hunters that prey on insects, worms, and other small animals.

Fire salamander can breathe through its skin

Skin produces a powerful poison

Frogs and toads
With their tail-less bodies, long hind legs, and big eyes, these amphibians are unmistakable. Many live on the ground, but others, like this tropical poison frog, hunt high in the trees. Most frogs start life as aquatic tadpoles that turn into air-breathing adults.

Picture questions
Every quiz has at least two picture questions, testing your visual memory.

How to use this book
Each quiz is given a difficulty rating – easy (green), medium (blue), or hard (red) – as well as a quiz number. The questions are also numbered, with multiple-choice answers. Each question is colour-coded, so you know which reference page to turn to if you want to find out more about a particular subject. The answers are laid out in a clear, easy-to-use section at the back of the book.

Learning more
You'll find fun facts on every page.

Difficulty rating
Choose between easy, medium, and hard quizzes, depending on how bright you're feeling. The level of each quiz is clearly indicated.

Difficulty level: Easy

12 Where are the forests in which mammoths and tamarins live?

13 Some lizards distract predators by doing what?

14 This animal is found on every continent except...

15 Which bird, often seen on Christmas cards, is a member of the order Passeriformes?

Chinese used fireflies in jars as lanterns

7 In its symbiotic relationship with an anemone, the clownfish provides...

8 How many eggs can a female oyster produce in a lifetime?

How many eggs can a chicken lay in 24 hours?

Where do the larvae of caddis flies live?

Difficulty level: Hard

11 Belugas are well camouflaged for life in the ice caps. What are belugas?

12 What is a young beaver called?

13 How many eggs can a queen bee lay in a day?

14 Which birds from the Galapagos Islands were perhaps more influential on Darwin's ideas than the finches?

15 How does a stonefish defend itself against predators?

16 Which invertebrates could survive exposure to outer space?

17 When a vulture feels threatened, what might it do?

18 A single prairie dog town may be home to how many animals?

19 The skin of this bear is...

20 Frog tadpoles are vegetarian, but later they eat other organisms, including other tadpoles. They change from...

Reference

lizards
...rd is a reptile, usually with four legs and a long ...but some are legless. Scaly, waterproof skins... lizards live in dry places, but like amphibians ...y are cold-blooded animals that need warm ...ather to stay active. So most lizards, such as this ...diterranean chameleon, live in warm climates.

Tough, horny scales protect skin

Turtles and tortoises
The massive, arching shells that protect their bodies make turtles and tortoises quite unlike other reptiles. The tortoises are famous for their slowness, but the green sea turtle is a swift swimmer.

Reference colour
Match the colour of the question to the colour of the reference page tab, and find out more about the subjects that interest you.

97 per cent of all known species

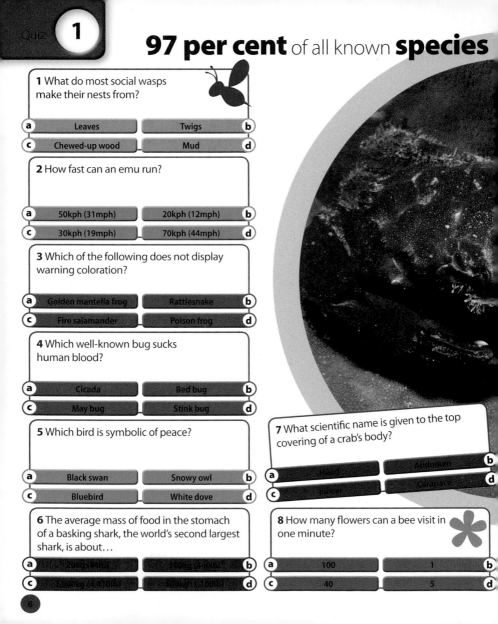

1 What do most social wasps make their nests from?

- **a** Leaves
- **b** Twigs
- **c** Chewed-up wood
- **d** Mud

2 How fast can an emu run?

- **a** 50kph (31mph)
- **b** 20kph (12mph)
- **c** 30kph (19mph)
- **d** 70kph (44mph)

3 Which of the following does not display warning coloration?

- **a** Golden mantella frog
- **b** Rattlesnake
- **c** Fire salamander
- **d** Poison frog

4 Which well-known bug sucks human blood?

- **a** Cicada
- **b** Bed bug
- **c** May bug
- **d** Stink bug

5 Which bird is symbolic of peace?

- **a** Black swan
- **b** Snowy owl
- **c** Bluebird
- **d** White dove

6 The average mass of food in the stomach of a basking shark, the world's second largest shark, is about…

- **a** 20kg (44lb)
- **b** 200kg (440lb)
- **c** 2,000kg (4,410lb)
- **d** 500kg (1,100lb)

7 What scientific name is given to the top covering of a crab's body?

- **a** Hood
- **b** Abdomen
- **c** Pincer
- **d** Carapace

8 How many flowers can a bee visit in one minute?

- **a** 100
- **b** 1
- **c** 40
- **d** 5

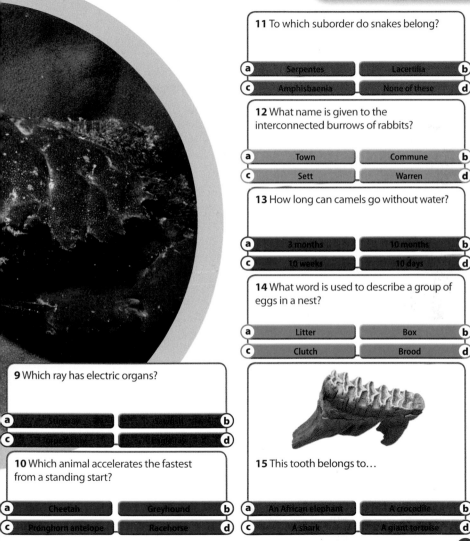

11 To which suborder do snakes belong?

(a) Serpentes (b) Lacertilia
(c) Amphisbaenia (d) None of these

12 What name is given to the interconnected burrows of rabbits?

(a) Town (b) Commune
(c) Sett (d) Warren

13 How long can camels go without water?

(a) 3 months (b) 10 months
(c) 10 weeks (d) 10 days

14 What word is used to describe a group of eggs in a nest?

(a) Litter (b) Box
(c) Clutch (d) Brood

9 Which ray has electric organs?

(a) Stingray (b) Sawfish
(c) Torpedo ray (d) Eagle ray

10 Which animal accelerates the fastest from a standing start?

(a) Cheetah (b) Greyhound
(c) Pronghorn antelope (d) Racehorse

15 This tooth belongs to…

(a) An African elephant (b) A crocodile
(c) A shark (d) A giant tortoise

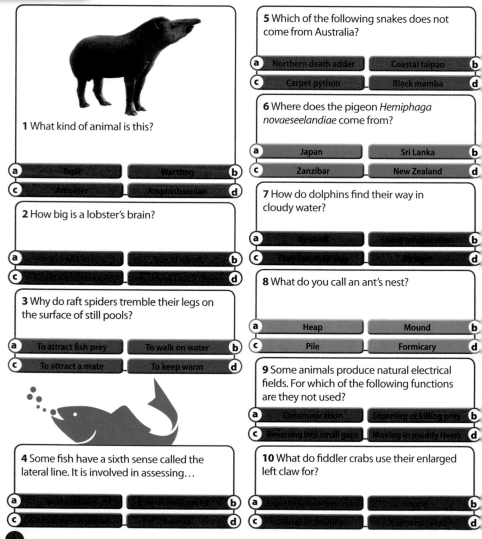

1 What kind of animal is this?

a Tapir	**b** Warthog
c Anteater	**d** Amphisbaenian

2 How big is a lobster's brain?

a	**b**
c	**d**

3 Why do raft spiders tremble their legs on the surface of still pools?

a To attract fish prey	**b** To walk on water
c To attract a mate	**d** To keep warm

4 Some fish have a sixth sense called the lateral line. It is involved in assessing…

a	**b**
c	**d**

5 Which of the following snakes does not come from Australia?

a Northern death adder	**b** Coastal taipan
c Carpet python	**d** Black mamba

6 Where does the pigeon *Hemiphaga novaeseelandiae* come from?

a Japan	**b** Sri Lanka
c Zanzibar	**d** New Zealand

7 How do dolphins find their way in cloudy water?

a By smell	**b** Using echolocation
c They feel their way	**d** By luck

8 What do you call an ant's nest?

a Heap	**b** Mound
c Pile	**d** Formicary

9 Some animals produce natural electrical fields. For which of the following functions are they not used?

a Communication	**b** Stunning or killing prey
c Reversing into small gaps	**d** Moving in muddy rivers

10 What do fiddler crabs use their enlarged left claw for?

a Signalling to other crabs	**b** Eating
c Helping in moulting	**d** Catching prey

11 A fly tastes sugary food with its…

a) Legs
b) Tongue
c) Wings
d) Nose

12 What shape are the bite marks of a cookiecutter shark?

a)
b)
c)
d)

13 Why is the midwife toad so named?

a) Both sexes tend eggs
b) Females carry eggs
c) Males carry eggs
d) Females nest together

14 Which of these do birds not use to help guide them during migration?

a) Built-in magnet
b) Landmarks
c) The Sun
d) Smell

15 What food do gelada baboons specialize in eating?

a) Nuts
b) Grass
c) Fruit
d) Termites

16 Which marine habitat contains the most animal species?

a) Ocean trenches
b) Coral reef
c) Deep ocean
d) Twilight zone

17 Which of the following is not used to describe grey coloration in horses?

a) Dapple
b) Fleabitten
c) Iron
d) Flaxen

18 Sociable weavers are so named because they…

a) Congregate to breed
b) Are non-aggressive
c) Feed others' young
d) Build communal nests

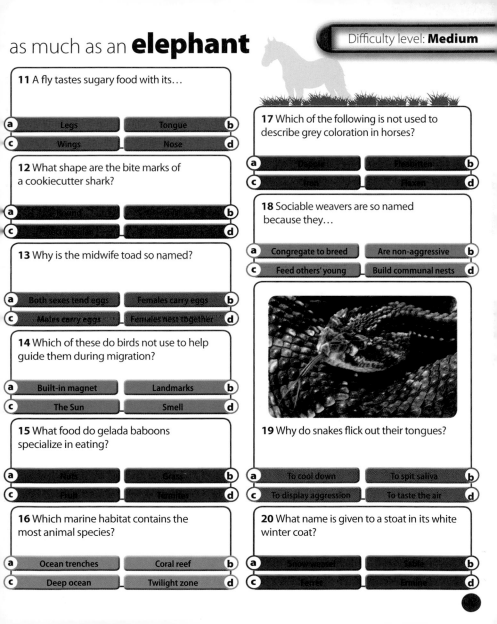

19 Why do snakes flick out their tongues?

a) To cool down
b) To spit saliva
c) To display aggression
d) To taste the air

20 What name is given to a stoat in its white winter coat?

a) Snow weasel
b) Sable
c) Ferret
d) Ermine

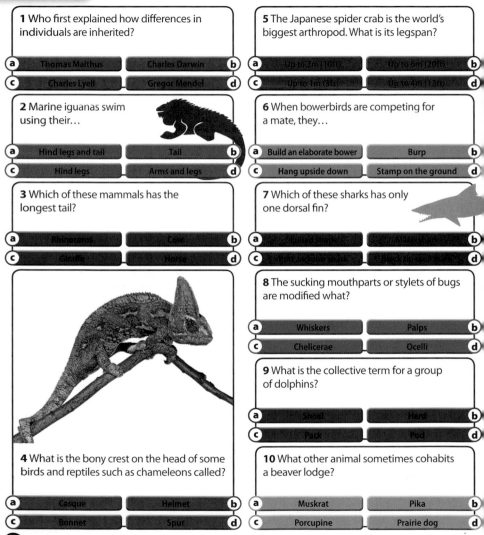

1 Who first explained how differences in individuals are inherited?

- **a** Thomas Malthus
- **b** Charles Darwin
- **c** Charles Lyell
- **d** Gregor Mendel

2 Marine iguanas swim using their…

- **a** Hind legs and tail
- **b** Tail
- **c** Hind legs
- **d** Arms and legs

3 Which of these mammals has the longest tail?

- **a** Rhinoceros
- **b** Cow
- **c** Giraffe
- **d** Horse

4 What is the bony crest on the head of some birds and reptiles such as chameleons called?

- **a** Casque
- **b** Helmet
- **c** Bonnet
- **d** Spur

5 The Japanese spider crab is the world's biggest arthropod. What is its legspan?

- **a** Up to 3m (10ft)
- **b** Up to 6m (20ft)
- **c** Up to 1m (3ft)
- **d** Up to 4m (13ft)

6 When bowerbirds are competing for a mate, they…

- **a** Build an elaborate bower
- **b** Burp
- **c** Hang upside down
- **d** Stamp on the ground

7 Which of these sharks has only one dorsal fin?

- **a** Frilled Shark
- **b** Mako Shark
- **c** Port Jackson Shark
- **d** Black-tipped Shark

8 The sucking mouthparts or stylets of bugs are modified what?

- **a** Whiskers
- **b** Palps
- **c** Chelicerae
- **d** Ocelli

9 What is the collective term for a group of dolphins?

- **a** Shoal
- **b** Herd
- **c** Pack
- **d** Pod

10 What other animal sometimes cohabits a beaver lodge?

- **a** Muskrat
- **b** Pika
- **c** Porcupine
- **d** Prairie dog

before the dinosaurs

11 A bed bug is an…

- a Endoparasite
- b Exoparasite
- c Alloparasite
- d Ectoparasite

12 The Madagascan aye-aye extracts grubs from crevices in dead wood using a…

- a Long, sticky tongue
- b Long, curved fang
- c Long, skinny finger
- d Sharpened stick

13 What is the collective name for a group of cobras?

- a Army
- b Swarm
- c Gulp
- d Quiver

14 Which fish, introduced to Lake Victoria, created an ecological disaster?

- a Nile perch
- b Paddlefish
- c Barramundi
- d Arapaima

15 Which of these are limbless amphibians?

- a Annelids
- b Adenophoreans
- c Caecilians
- d Amphisbaenians

16 Who was the first to use the phrase "survival of the fittest"?

- a Charles Darwin
- b Alfred Russel Wallace
- c Georges Cuvier
- d Herbert Spencer

17 By which process does a hydra reproduce asexually?

- a Spores
- b Budding
- c Splitting in two
- d Fragmentation

18 The individual animals that make up a coral reef are known as…

- a Radula
- b Polyps
- c Clones
- d Spicules

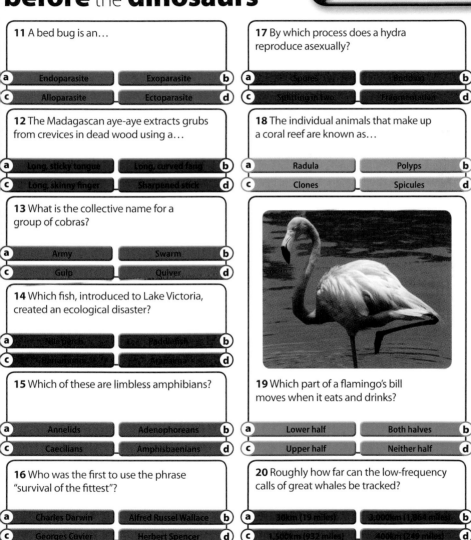

19 Which part of a flamingo's bill moves when it eats and drinks?

- a Lower half
- b Both halves
- c Upper half
- d Neither half

20 Roughly how far can the low-frequency calls of great whales be tracked?

- a 30km (19 miles)
- b 3,000km (1,864 miles)
- c 1,500km (932 miles)
- d 400km (249 miles)

A **bald eagle** has about

1 How long is a giraffe's tongue?

(a) 18cm (7in)
(b) 10cm (4in)
(c) 32cm (13in)
(d) 46cm (18in)

2 How many pairs of jointed walking legs does a spider have?

(a) 3
(b) 5
(c) 4
(d) 2

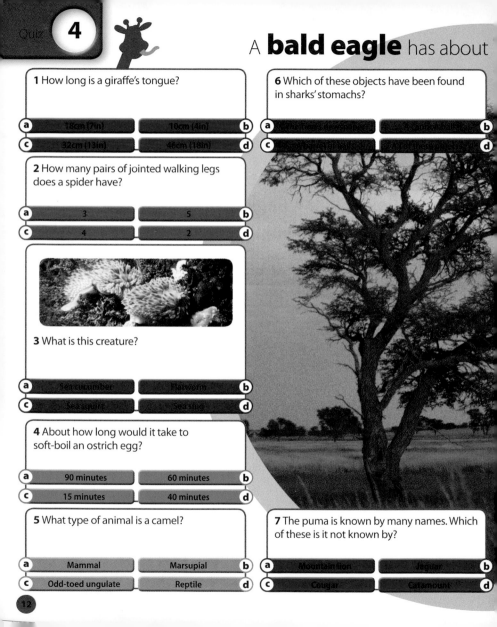

3 What is this creature?

(a) Sea cucumber
(b) Flatworm
(c) Sea squirt
(d) Sea slug

4 About how long would it take to soft-boil an ostrich egg?

(a) 90 minutes
(b) 60 minutes
(c) 15 minutes
(d) 40 minutes

5 What type of animal is a camel?

(a) Mammal
(b) Marsupial
(c) Odd-toed ungulate
(d) Reptile

6 Which of these objects have been found in sharks' stomachs?

(a) A few stamps
(b) A tennis ball
(c) A piece of wood
(d) All of the above

7 The puma is known by many names. Which of these is it not known by?

(a) Mountain lion
(b) Jaguar
(c) Cougar
(d) Catamount

7,200 feathers

8 Where in the world would you find an anaconda?

a Asia	**b** Australia
c S America	**d** Europe

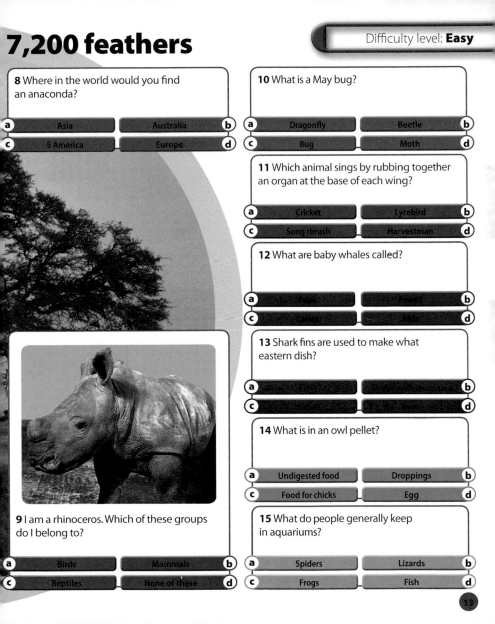

9 I am a rhinoceros. Which of these groups do I belong to?

a Birds	**b** Mammals
c Reptiles	**d** None of these

10 What is a May bug?

a Dragonfly	**b** Beetle
c Bug	**d** Moth

11 Which animal sings by rubbing together an organ at the base of each wing?

a Cricket	**b** Lyrebird
c Song thrush	**d** Harvestman

12 What are baby whales called?

a Pups	**b** Fawns
c Calves	**d** Kids

13 Shark fins are used to make what eastern dish?

a	**b**
c	**d**

14 What is in an owl pellet?

a Undigested food	**b** Droppings
c Food for chicks	**d** Egg

15 What do people generally keep in aquariums?

a Spiders	**b** Lizards
c Frogs	**d** Fish

1 Which of the following would not be found in a mangrove swamp?

a) Flamingo
b) Fiddler crab
c) Mudskipper
d) Bulldog bat

2 The spicules (tiny spikes) in calcareous sponges are made from what?

a) Calcium and silicon
b) Silicon
c) Calcium carbonate
d) None of these

3 How many feet does a snail have?

a) 3
b) 6
c) 2
d) 1

4 What makes the skin of a shark so rough to touch?

a) Keratin spikes
b) Chitin spines
c) Ripples on skin
d) Dermal denticles

5 Which of the following is a venomous lizard?

a) Monitor lizard
b) Leopard gecko
c) Gila monster
d) Red tegu

6 How do ring-tailed lemur troops settle boundary disputes?

a) With stink fights
b) With screaming contests
c) By fighting to the death
d) With wrestling matches

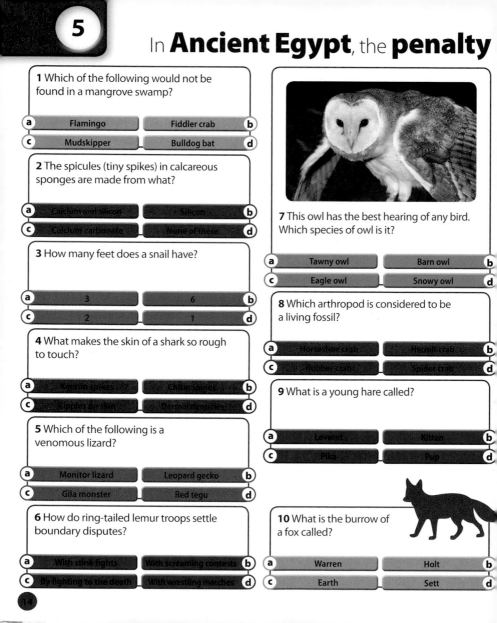

7 This owl has the best hearing of any bird. Which species of owl is it?

a) Tawny owl
b) Barn owl
c) Eagle owl
d) Snowy owl

8 Which arthropod is considered to be a living fossil?

a) Horseshoe crab
b) Hermit crab
c) Robber crab
d) Spider crab

9 What is a young hare called?

a) Leveret
b) Kitten
c) Pika
d) Pup

10 What is the burrow of a fox called?

a) Warren
b) Holt
c) Earth
d) Sett

11 How much blood can a typical leech consume in one meal?

a Half its body weight
b Twice its body weight
c 4 times its body weight
d 10 times its body weight

12 Which mammal has the biggest ears relative to its body size?

a Kangaroo rat
b Dog
c Fennec fox
d Elephant

13 Which plant did Mendel use for his inheritance experiments?

a Tulip
b Tomato
c Pea
d Geranium

14 Which is the smallest lizard in the world?

a Gecko
b Monitor
c Skink
d Chameleon

15 Which fish are known as "wolves of the sea"?

a Barracudas
b Sharks
c Rays
d Deep sea fish

16 Why are flamingos pink?

a Polluted rain
b We dye them
c Diet
d Genes

17 A cicada, like this one, has which type of diet?

a Herbivorous
b Omnivorous
c Carnivorous
d Detrivorous

18 Which of these birds keeps its eggs warm on top of its feet?

a Mallee fowl
b Bald eagle
c Emperor penguin
d Ostrich

19 Who leads a herd of elephants?

a There is no leader
b The oldest female
c The biggest male
d A coalition of males

20 Which of the following can have the most eyes?

a Spider
b Starfish
c Earthworm
d Crab

1 In Greek mythology, the Minotaur has the head of which animal?

a Fox
b Lion
c Bull
d Stag

2 A predator is always…

a Larger than its prey
b Toothed
c A killer
d Swift

3 Where is the spiny orb-weaving spider found?

a Asia
b Europe
c Australia
d N America

4 Which European animal did white settlers in Australia mistake the wombat for?

a Rabbit
b Badger
c Bear
d Giant vole

5 About how many species of bony fish are there?

a
b
c
d

6 What is the collective name for a group of tortoises?

a Gang
b Walk
c Turn
d Herd

7 Which of the following is not a type of fish scale?

a Ctenoid
b Cycloid
c Placoid
d Ganoid

8 How long does it take for a blue-ringed octopus's bite to kill a human?

a 15 minutes
b 2 hours
c 24 days
d It is not venomous

9 Where are the glands that produce the foul-smelling substance from which stink bugs get their name?

a Thorax
b Abdomen
c Head
d Legs

10 Which of the following is most closely related to the magpie?

a Carrion crow
b Dove
c Swan
d Owl

11 How many species of snake are vegetarian?

a) 5
b) None, they all eat meat
c) 1
d) All of them

12 Which bird spends more time in the air than any other?

a) Wandering albatross
b) Puffin
c) Sooty tern
d) Arctic tern

13 Exploitation of which fish led to the decline of Cannery Row in California?

a) Pacific salmon
b) Halibut
c) Sea bass
d) Sardine

14 Which mammal has the warmest fur?

a) Yak
b) Arctic fox
c) Snowshoe hare
d) Harp seal

15 Which of the following is not necessary for evolution to happen?

a) Competition for food
b) Surplus offspring
c) Desire to change
d) Genetic variation

16 A desert locust swarm can cover 1,200 square km (460 square miles). How many locusts make up such a swarm?

a) Up to 8 million
b) Up to 80,000
c) Up to 80 million
d) Up to 800,000

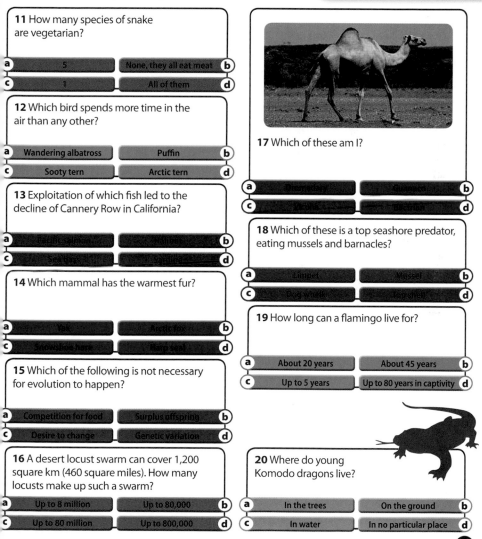

17 Which of these am I?

a) Dromedary
b) Guanaco
c) Alpaca
d) Bactrian

18 Which of these is a top seashore predator, eating mussels and barnacles?

a) Limpet
b) Mussel
c) Dog whelk
d) Top shell

19 How long can a flamingo live for?

a) About 20 years
b) About 45 years
c) Up to 5 years
d) Up to 80 years in captivity

20 Where do young Komodo dragons live?

a) In the trees
b) On the ground
c) In water
d) In no particular place

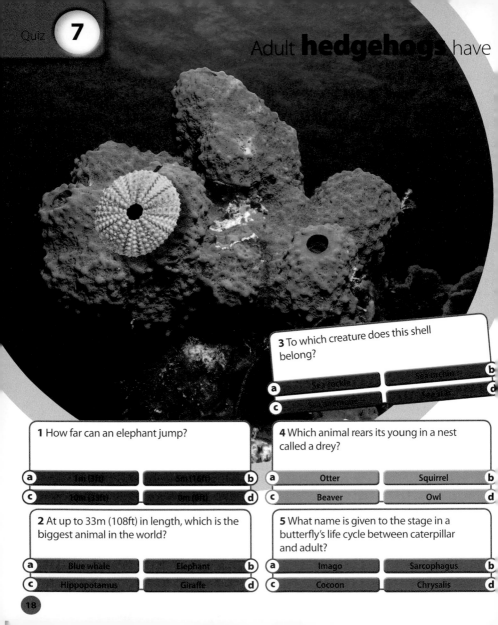

Adult **hedgehogs** have

3 To which creature does this shell belong?

a. Sea cockle
b. Sea urchin
c. Sea anemone
d. Sea star

1 How far can an elephant jump?

a. 1m (3ft)
b. 5m (16ft)
c. 10m (33ft)
d. 0m (0ft)

2 At up to 33m (108ft) in length, which is the biggest animal in the world?

a. Blue whale
b. Elephant
c. Hippopotamus
d. Giraffe

4 Which animal rears its young in a nest called a drey?

a. Otter
b. Squirrel
c. Beaver
d. Owl

5 What name is given to the stage in a butterfly's life cycle between caterpillar and adult?

a. Imago
b. Sarcophagus
c. Cocoon
d. Chrysalis

6 Which type of animal has a skeleton made of cartilage?

a Amphibian
b Bird
c Shark
d Reptile

7 Lungfish are found in all but one of these places. Which is it?

a Africa
b S America
c Europe
d Australia

8 How many pairs of legs does an insect have?

a 3
b 2
c 4
d 5

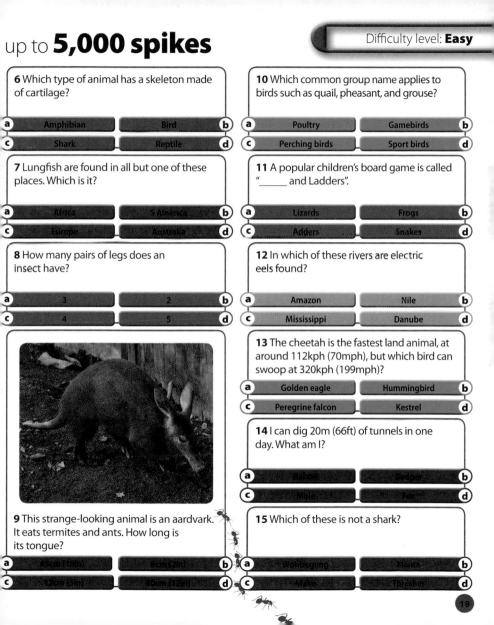

9 This strange-looking animal is an aardvark. It eats termites and ants. How long is its tongue?

a 45cm (18in)
b 5cm (2in)
c 12cm (5in)
d 30cm (12in)

10 Which common group name applies to birds such as quail, pheasant, and grouse?

a Poultry
b Gamebirds
c Perching birds
d Sport birds

11 A popular children's board game is called "_____ and Ladders".

a Lizards
b Frogs
c Adders
d Snakes

12 In which of these rivers are electric eels found?

a Amazon
b Nile
c Mississippi
d Danube

13 The cheetah is the fastest land animal, at around 112kph (70mph), but which bird can swoop at 320kph (199mph)?

a Golden eagle
b Hummingbird
c Peregrine falcon
d Kestrel

14 I can dig 20m (66ft) of tunnels in one day. What am I?

a Rabbit
b Badger
c Mole
d Fox

15 Which of these is not a shark?

a Wobbegong
b Manta
c Mako
d Thresher

1 How do most marine snails move?

- **a** Actively swim
- **b** Glide on a muscular foot
- **c** Drift in the water
- **d** They don't move

2 In which species is the male commonly eaten by the female after mating?

- **a** Redback spider
- **b** Wolf spider
- **c** Black widow spider
- **d** Funnel-web spider

3 What does a jawfish do to keep its eggs safe from predators?

- **a** It buries them in sand
- **b** It eats them until hatched
- **c** It carries them in its mouth
- **d** Makes a seaweed nest

4 How fast can a roadrunner run?

- **a** 80kph (50mph)
- **b** 24kph (15mph)
- **c** 32kph (20mph)
- **d** 40kph (25mph)

5 Alligators are native to the US and which other country?

- **a** Australia
- **b** China
- **c** Egypt
- **d** Brazil

6 How does a chinchilla keep its fine fur clean?

- **a** It grows a new coat weekly
- **b** It washes it in rain
- **c** It swims regularly
- **d** It takes dust baths

7 Which of these animals cannot close its nostrils?

- **a**
- **b**
- **c**
- **d**

8 Domestic animals like horses that have returned to the wild are described as being what?

- **a** Wild
- **b** Reverted
- **c** Feral
- **d** Escapees

9 What is the correct term for a wasp's nest?

- **a** Cell
- **b** Vespiary
- **c** Hive
- **d** Comb

10 About what percentage of animal species are insects?

- **a** 20 per cent
- **b** 60 per cent
- **c** 80 per cent
- **d** 40 per cent

11 Which of these birds builds the smallest cup nest?

a Starling
b Hummingbird
c Oriole
d Sparrow

12 How many pairs of antennae do crustaceans have?

a
b 2
c 1
d None

13 What is the correct term for the mating embrace of frogs?

a Grasping
b Amplexus
c Hugging
d Holding

14 Which group of birds does the capercaillie belong to?

a Passerines
b Birds of prey
c Gamebirds
d Waders

15 Which is the largest living marsupial meat-eater?

a Tasmanian wolf
b Tasmanian tiger
c Tasmanian dog
d Tasmanian devil

16 What colour do walruses turn after basking in the polar sunshine?

a Grey
b Black
c White
d Pink

17 The dormouse gets its name from the French word *dormir*, meaning "to sleep". How long does it hibernate for?

a 3–4 months
b More than 6 months
c 2 months
d 6–7 months

18 How many gill slits are present in most sharks?

a
b
c
d

19 Which is the world's largest jellyfish?

a Spotted lagoon jellyfish
b Portuguese man o' war
c Lion's mane jellyfish
d Moon jellyfish

20 What kind of animal is an abalone – the favourite food of a sea otter?

a Sea urchin
b Eel
c Mollusc
d Flatfish

The Ancient **Chinese** used **fireflies**

1 Which mammals have males known as hobs and females known as jills?

a) Ferrets
b) Foxes
c) Meerkats
d) Mongooses

2 Most reptiles lay eggs. What term is used for this?

a) Oviparous
b) Viviparous
c) Ovoviviparous
d) None of these

3 Which of the following is not a stage in the life cycle of a salmon?

a) Smolt
b) Alevin
c) Larva
d) Parr

4 If predator numbers are higher than prey numbers, the predators will…

a) Interbreed
b) Decrease in number
c) Increase in number
d) Stay the same

5 At what age do baby hooded seals become independent?

a) 5 days
b) 13 days
c) 4 weeks
d) 6 months

6 Which of the following is not a type of snake locomotion?

a) Lateral undulation
b) Creeping
c) Sidewinding
d) Concertina

7 In its symbiotic relationship with an anemone, the clownfish provides…

a) Companionship
b) Camouflage
c) Removal of parasites
d) Protection

8 How many eggs can a female oyster produce in a lifetime?

a) About 100,000
b) About 100 million
c) About 20
d) About 100

9 How many eggs can a chicken lay in 24 hours?

a) 6
b) 12
c) 1
d) 2

10 Where do the larvae of caddis flies live?

a) In the soil
b) Under rocks
c) Underground
d) In water

in **jars** as **lanterns**

11 Belugas are well camouflaged for life in the ice caps. What are belugas?

a | White rabbits
b | White foxes
c | White birds
d | White whales

12 What is a young beaver called?

a | Kitten
b | Pup
c | Cub
d | Calf

13 How many eggs can a queen bee lay in a day?

a | Up to 20
b | Up to 2,000
c | 1
d | Up to 200

14 Which birds from the Galapagos Islands were perhaps more influential on Darwin's ideas than the finches?

a | Storm petrels
b | Mockingbirds
c | Tropic birds
d | Boobies

15 How does a stonefish defend itself against predators?

a | It loses its tail
b | It plays dead
c | Poisonous spines
d | Sharp teeth

16 Which invertebrates could survive exposure to outer space?

a | Polar bears
b | Krill
c | Crabs
d | Jellyfish

17 When a vulture feels threatened, what might it do?

a | Fly away quickly
b | Run and hide
c | Huddle with others
d | Vomit and shake its head

18 A single prairie dog town may be home to how many animals?

a | 500,000
b | 400 million
c | 20 million
d | 200,000

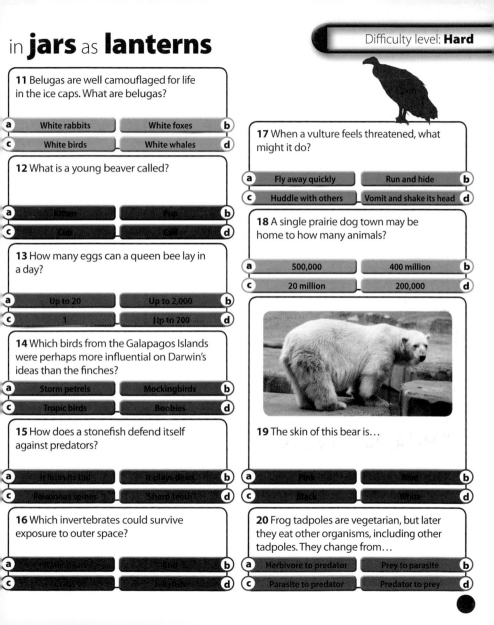

19 The skin of this bear is…

a | Pink
b | Blue
c | Black
d | White

20 Frog tadpoles are vegetarian, but later they eat other organisms, including other tadpoles. They change from…

a | Herbivore to predator
b | Prey to parasite
c | Parasite to predator
d | Predator to prey

Giant pandas spend up to **14** hours

1 With the help of others, I can build a nest up to 7m (23ft) high. What am I?

- **a** Ant
- **b** Bee
- **c** Termite
- **d** Wasp

2 Which animal uses jet propulsion?

- **a** Sparrowhawk
- **b** Torpedo ray
- **c** Squid
- **d** Sea squirt

3 What do you call an insect that resembles another to avoid being eaten?

- **a** Symbiont
- **b** Parasite
- **c** Mate
- **d** Mimic

4 Which of these mammals is not a carnivore?

- **a** Weasel
- **b** Raccoon
- **c** Leopard
- **d** Tamarin monkey

5 Frogs' eggs are collectively called what?

- **a** Spawn
- **b** Clutch
- **c** Batch
- **d** Ova

6 In the animated film *Finding Nemo*, what type of fish is Nemo?

- **a** Anglerfish
- **b** Sharksucker
- **c** Clownfish
- **d** Blenny

7 What is the correct term for a group of wolves?

- **a** Pack
- **b** Team
- **c** Clan
- **d** Pride

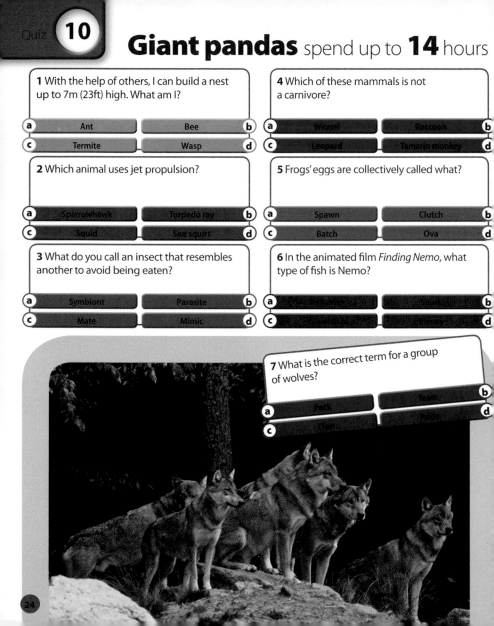

each day eating **bamboo**

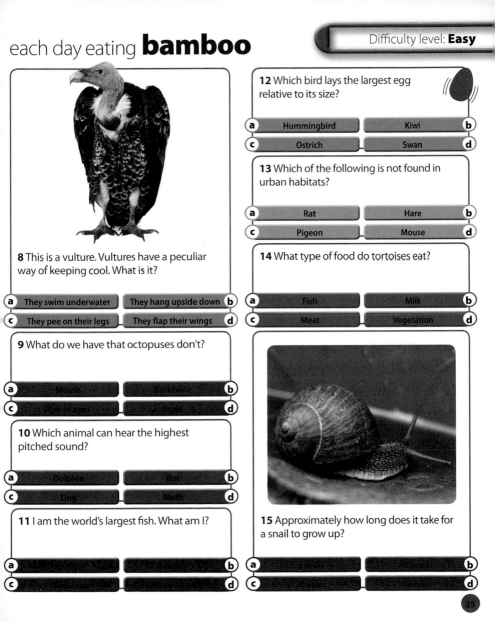

8 This is a vulture. Vultures have a peculiar way of keeping cool. What is it?

a They swim underwater | b They hang upside down
c They pee on their legs | d They flap their wings

9 What do we have that octopuses don't?

a Mouth | b Backbone
c Pair of eyes | d Brain

10 Which animal can hear the highest pitched sound?

a Dolphin | b Bat
c Dog | d Moth

11 I am the world's largest fish. What am I?

a | b
c | d

12 Which bird lays the largest egg relative to its size?

a Hummingbird | b Kiwi
c Ostrich | d Swan

13 Which of the following is not found in urban habitats?

a Rat | b Hare
c Pigeon | d Mouse

14 What type of food do tortoises eat?

a Fish | b Milk
c Meat | d Vegetation

15 Approximately how long does it take for a snail to grow up?

a 1 year | b 10 years
c 20 years | d 2 weeks

A **dolphin** is **born** with a moustache

1 Nematode worms are the most abundant animals in many soils. A square metre can contain how many?

- (a) Several hundred
- (b) Several million
- (c) Several thousand
- (d) Hundreds of thousands

2 Some animals have infrared sensors, which they use to identify…

- (a) The presence of plants
- (b) Heat from possible prey
- (c) Hot rocks for warmth
- (d) Light from the Moon

3 How does a giraffe clean its ears?

- (a) It washes while drinking
- (b) It rubs its head in dust
- (c) With its long tongue
- (d) Birds pick out the dirt

4 Which of these sharks lives on the sea bed?

- (a) The great white shark
- (b) It's an angel shark
- (c) The tiger shark
- (d) It has long hair

5 During metamorphosis, what stage follows the hatching of the egg?

- (a) Drone
- (b) Larva
- (c) Pupa
- (d) Imago

6 How do snakes find their partners?

- (a) From their scent
- (b) By temperature
- (c) By light
- (d) With a courtship dance

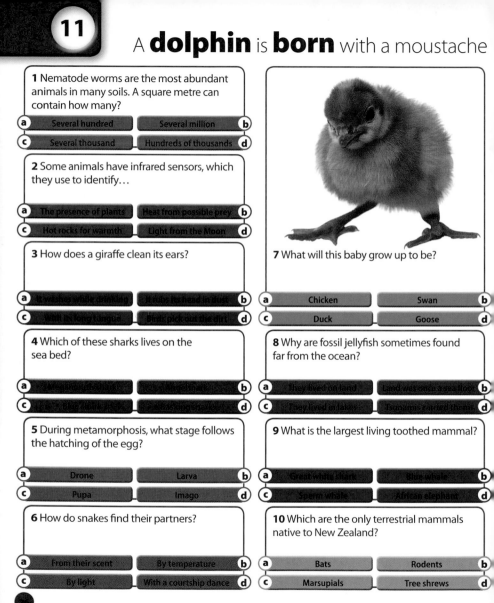

7 What will this baby grow up to be?

- (a) Chicken
- (b) Swan
- (c) Duck
- (d) Goose

8 Why are fossil jellyfish sometimes found far from the ocean?

- (a) They lived on land
- (b) Land was once a sea floor
- (c) They lived in lakes
- (d) Tsunamis carried them

9 What is the largest living toothed mammal?

- (a) Great white shark
- (b) Blue whale
- (c) Sperm whale
- (d) African elephant

10 Which are the only terrestrial mammals native to New Zealand?

- (a) Bats
- (b) Rodents
- (c) Marsupials
- (d) Tree shrews

to **help** it **feel** its mother

11 How many species of rhinoceros are there?

a. 2
b. 4
c. 5
d. 3

12 How many eggs does a saltwater crocodile generally lay?

a. Between 10 and 30
b. Less than 10
c. More than 100
d. Between 40 and 60

13 Which of these echinoderms belongs to the class Asteroidea?

a. Sea daisies
b. Sea cucumbers
c. Sea urchins
d. Starfish

14 How long ago did birds evolve?

a. 150 million years
b. 200 million years
c. 100 million years
d. 65 million years

15 In which habitat would you find a chamois?

a. Mountains
b. Grassland
c. Rainforest
d. Taiga

16 Why are African sengis also known as elephant shrews?

a. They have long snouts
b. They are very large
c. They have tusks
d. They eat elephant dung

17 In which part of the gut do birds grind down food?

a. Gizzard
b. Crop
c. Bill
d. Oesophagus

18 What type of arthropod carries Lyme disease?

a. Spider
b. Beetle
c. Mosquito
d. Tick

19 Cod is currently under threat from what?

a. Global warming
b. Disease
c. Loss of habitat
d. Overfishing

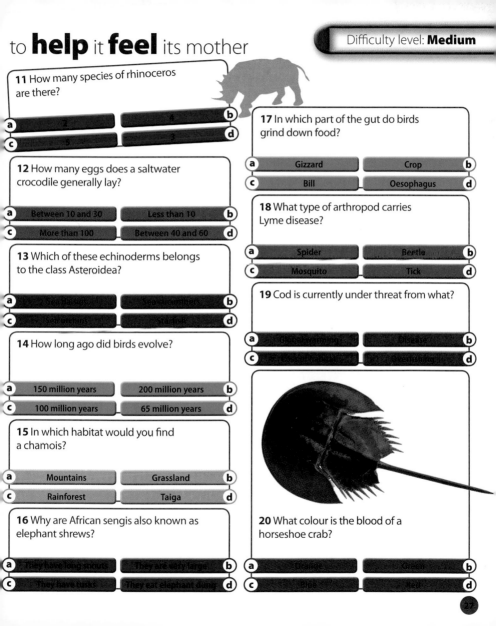

20 What colour is the blood of a horseshoe crab?

a. Orange
b. Green
c. Blue
d. Red

1 About how heavy is a male elephant seal compared to a female?

- **a** They weigh the same
- **b** Half as heavy
- **c** Twice as heavy
- **d** 3 times as heavy

2 Where are whip-spiders found?

- **a** In deciduous forests
- **b** In the Antarctic
- **c** In caves
- **d** In attics

3 Which crab carries sea anemones on its claws to fend off predators?

- **a** Robber crab
- **b** Hermit crab
- **c** Fiddler crab
- **d** Boxer crab

4 How many toes does an ostrich have on each foot?

- **a** None
- **b** 2
- **c** 3
- **d** 4

5 Where does the grunion lay its eggs?

- **a** On a branch
- **b** On sand beaches
- **c** In the riverbed
- **d** In deep water mud

6 The pistol shrimp disables its prey by…

- **a** Making a loud sound
- **b** Shooting water
- **c** Sharing it
- **d** Using a smokescreen

7 The goliath frog is the world's largest frog. How heavy are the biggest specimens?

- **a** 3kg (7lb)
- **b** 7kg (15lb)
- **c** 1kg (2lb)
- **d** 4kg (9lb)

8 What are the gills of bony fishes covered with?

- **a** Large scales
- **b** A flap
- **c** Sharp spines
- **d** Operculum

9 What is the collective name for a group of crocodiles?

- **a** Congregation
- **b** Troop
- **c** Colony
- **d** Band

10 In George Orwell's *Animal Farm*, what sort of animal is Napoleon?

- **a** Goat
- **b** Pig
- **c** Horse
- **d** Donkey

11 How many individual lenses make up the large compound eye of a dragonfly?

| a | More than 10,000 | About 1,500 | b |
| c | About 7,000 | About 300 | d |

12 Which of these animals has digitigrade locomotion?

| a | Gazelle | Giant panda | b |
| c | Bat | Cheetah | d |

13 Besides the duck-billed platypus, which other mammals lay eggs?

| a | None | Opossums | b |
| c | Wallabies | Echidnas | d |

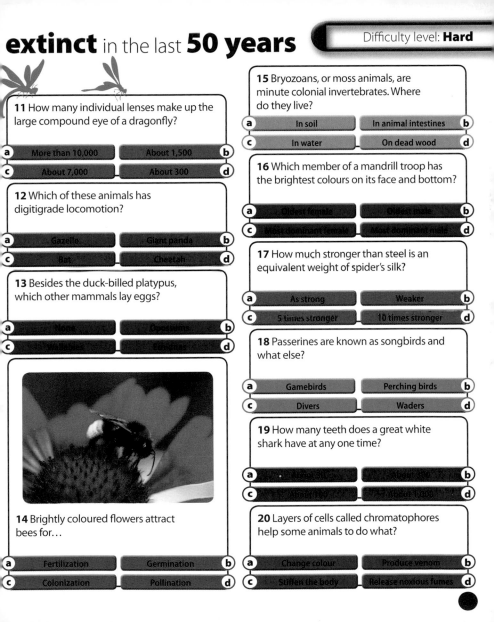

14 Brightly coloured flowers attract bees for…

| a | Fertilization | Germination | b |
| c | Colonization | Pollination | d |

15 Bryozoans, or moss animals, are minute colonial invertebrates. Where do they live?

| a | In soil | In animal intestines | b |
| c | In water | On dead wood | d |

16 Which member of a mandrill troop has the brightest colours on its face and bottom?

| a | Oldest female | Oldest male | b |
| c | Most dominant female | Most dominant male | d |

17 How much stronger than steel is an equivalent weight of spider's silk?

| a | As strong | Weaker | b |
| c | 5 times stronger | 10 times stronger | d |

18 Passerines are known as songbirds and what else?

| a | Gamebirds | Perching birds | b |
| c | Divers | Waders | d |

19 How many teeth does a great white shark have at any one time?

| a | About 50 | About 400 | b |
| c | About 100 | About 1,000 | d |

20 Layers of cells called chromatophores help some animals to do what?

| a | Change colour | Produce venom | b |
| c | Stiffen the body | Release noxious fumes | d |

A **spitting cobra's venom** can

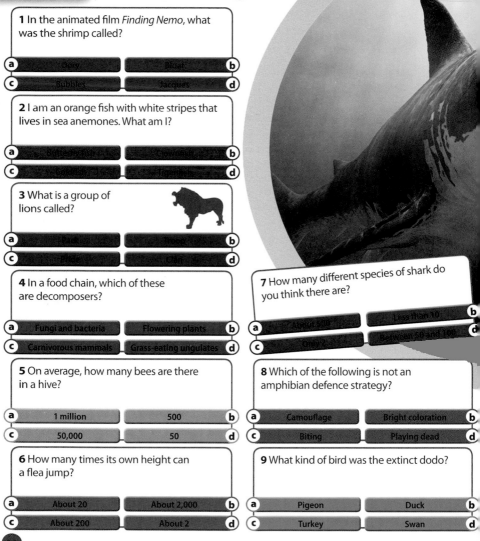

1 In the animated film *Finding Nemo*, what was the shrimp called?

a Dory
b Bloat
c Bubbles
d Jacques

2 I am an orange fish with white stripes that lives in sea anemones. What am I?

a Butterflyfish
b Clownfish
c Goldfish
d Tigerfish

3 What is a group of lions called?

a Pack
b Troop
c Pride
d Clan

4 In a food chain, which of these are decomposers?

a Fungi and bacteria
b Flowering plants
c Carnivorous mammals
d Grass-eating ungulates

5 On average, how many bees are there in a hive?

a 1 million
b 500
c 50,000
d 50

6 How many times its own height can a flea jump?

a About 20
b About 2,000
c About 200
d About 2

7 How many different species of shark do you think there are?

a About 500
b Less than 10
c Only 2
d Between 50 and 100

8 Which of the following is not an amphibian defence strategy?

a Camouflage
b Bright coloration
c Biting
d Playing dead

9 What kind of bird was the extinct dodo?

a Pigeon
b Duck
c Turkey
d Swan

12 Where are the forests in which marmosets and tamarins live?

(a) Central America

(b) Asia

(c) Africa

(d) S America

13 Some lizards distract predators by doing what?

(a) Hissing and spitting

(b) Shedding their tail

(c) Producing a foul smell

(d) Playing dead

10 How do bees tell each other where to find nectar?

(a) They leave a trail

(b) They dance

(c) They buzz

(d) They follow one another

11 Mammals that carry their young in pouches in their bodies are called…

(a) Primates

(b) Marsupials

(c) Monotremes

(d) Rodents

14 This animal is found on every continent except…

(a) Antarctica and Australia

(b) Europe

(c) Africa

(d) Asia

15 Which bird, often seen on Christmas cards, is a member of the order Passeriformes?

(a) Dove

(b) Partridge

(c) Turkey

(d) European robin

Mammals are the **only** type

1 Which of these is the world's most widespread carnivore?

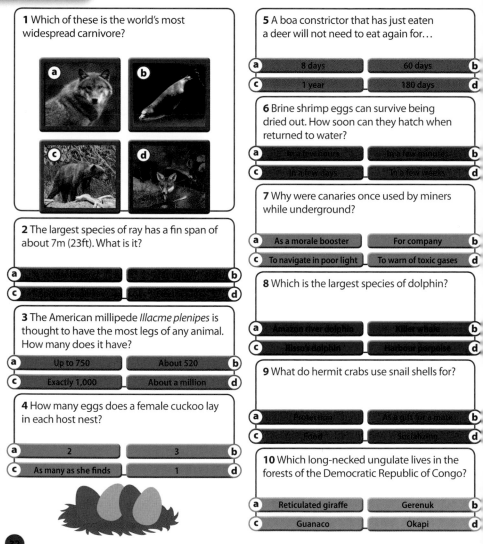

a
b
c
d

2 The largest species of ray has a fin span of about 7m (23ft). What is it?

a ▮▮▮▮▮▮▮▮ b
c ▮▮▮▮▮▮▮▮ d

3 The American millipede *Illacme plenipes* is thought to have the most legs of any animal. How many does it have?

| a | Up to 750 | About 520 | b |
| c | Exactly 1,000 | About a million | d |

4 How many eggs does a female cuckoo lay in each host nest?

| a | 2 | 3 | b |
| c | As many as she finds | 1 | d |

5 A boa constrictor that has just eaten a deer will not need to eat again for…

| a | 8 days | 60 days | b |
| c | 1 year | 180 days | d |

6 Brine shrimp eggs can survive being dried out. How soon can they hatch when returned to water?

| a | In a few hours | In a few minutes | b |
| c | In a few days | In a few weeks | d |

7 Why were canaries once used by miners while underground?

| a | As a morale booster | For company | b |
| c | To navigate in poor light | To warn of toxic gases | d |

8 Which is the largest species of dolphin?

| a | Amazon river dolphin | Killer whale | b |
| c | Risso's dolphin | Harbour porpoise | d |

9 What do hermit crabs use snail shells for?

| a | Protection | As a gift for a mate | b |
| c | Food | Socializing | d |

10 Which long-necked ungulate lives in the forests of the Democratic Republic of Congo?

| a | Reticulated giraffe | Gerenuk | b |
| c | Guanaco | Okapi | d |

of **animals** that **chew**

11 Which order includes butterflies and moths?

a Lepidoptera
b Phasmatodea
c Diptera
d Hymenoptera

12 How many insects can a giant anteater slurp up in a day using its long, sticky tongue?

a About 30
b About 30,000
c About 500
d About 1 million

13 When was the megamouth shark discovered?

a 1876
b 1945
c 2000
d 1976

14 Which of the following is not a colour seen in juvenile green tree pythons?

a Green
b Red
c Orange
d Yellow

15 Why do gray whales migrate south to Baja, California, each year?

a To feed
b To escape cold weather
c To breed
d All of these

16 Which breed of cat has a naturally short tail?

a Devon Rex
b Manx
c Scottish Fold
d Turkish Van

17 Which member of the parrot family cannot fly?

a Pileated parrot
b Kakapo
c Rainbow lorikeet
d Large fig parrot

18 What does the crown-of-thorns starfish feed on?

a
b
c
d

19 Which animal has the Latin name *Ursus maritimus*?

a Leopard seal
b Polar bear
c
d

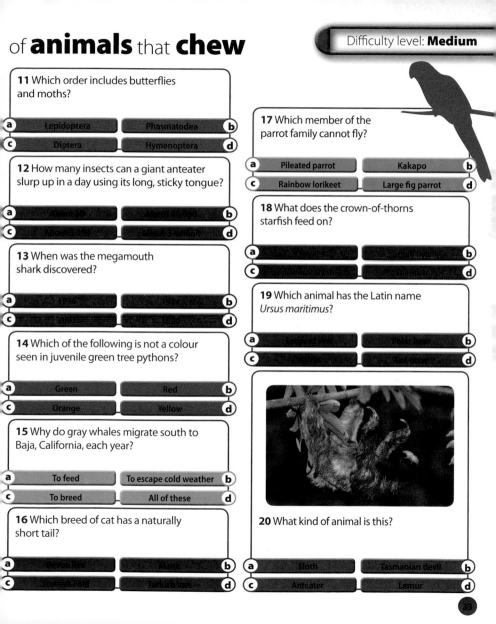

20 What kind of animal is this?

a Sloth
b Tasmanian devil
c Anteater
d Lemur

Snakes have **more bones**

1 How far can a flying fish glide?

(a) Up to 200m (650ft)
(b) Up to 73m (240ft)
(c) 200m to 1km (1451ft)
(d) Up to 305m (1000ft)

2 Which of these apes has shown the greatest flair for sign language?

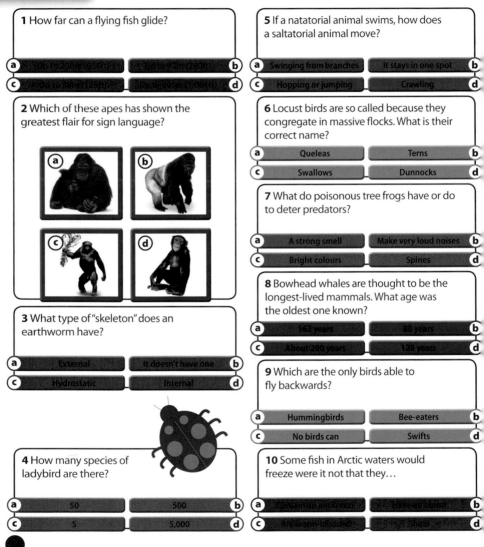

(a)
(b)
(c)
(d)

3 What type of "skeleton" does an earthworm have?

(a) External
(b) It doesn't have one
(c) Hydrostatic
(d) Internal

4 How many species of ladybird are there?

(a) 50
(b) 500
(c) 5
(d) 5,000

5 If a natatorial animal swims, how does a saltatorial animal move?

(a) Swinging from branches
(b) It stays in one spot
(c) Hopping or jumping
(d) Crawling

6 Locust birds are so called because they congregate in massive flocks. What is their correct name?

(a) Queleas
(b) Terns
(c) Swallows
(d) Dunnocks

7 What do poisonous tree frogs have or do to deter predators?

(a) A strong smell
(b) Make very loud noises
(c) Bright colours
(d) Spines

8 Bowhead whales are thought to be the longest-lived mammals. What age was the oldest one known?

(a) 162 years
(b) 80 years
(c) About 200 years
(d) 128 years

9 Which are the only birds able to fly backwards?

(a) Hummingbirds
(b) Bee-eaters
(c) No birds can
(d) Swifts

10 Some fish in Arctic waters would freeze were it not that they…

(a) Contain antifreeze
(b) Move to hotter
(c) Are warm-blooded
(d) Shoal

11 Which butterfly has the longest lifespan?

a Blue morpho
b Brimstone
c Swallowtail
d Monarch

12 The milksnake mimics the coloration of which venomous snake?

a Corn snake
b Long-nosed snake
c Pine snake
d Coral snake

13 An animal that is adapted for digging and living underground Is called…

a Fossorial
b Aquatic
c Aerial
d Cursorial

14 The flying lemur glides between trees on a web of skin. How far can it travel in this way?

a About 20m (66ft)
b Up to 50m (164ft)
c Up to 1km (0.6 miles)
d Over 100m (328ft)

15 What does a leaf-nosed bat use its fleshy nose "leaf" for?

a Breathing in flight
b Tasting fruit
c Focusing echolocation calls
d Funnelling scent

16 Which is the world's rarest parrot?

a Red-and-green
b Blue-and-yellow
c Spix's
d Hyacinth

17 What is the alternative common name of the beluga whale?

a Narwhal
b Long-finned pilot whale
c Killer whale
d White whale

18 What colour is the ink produced by squid?

a
b
c
d

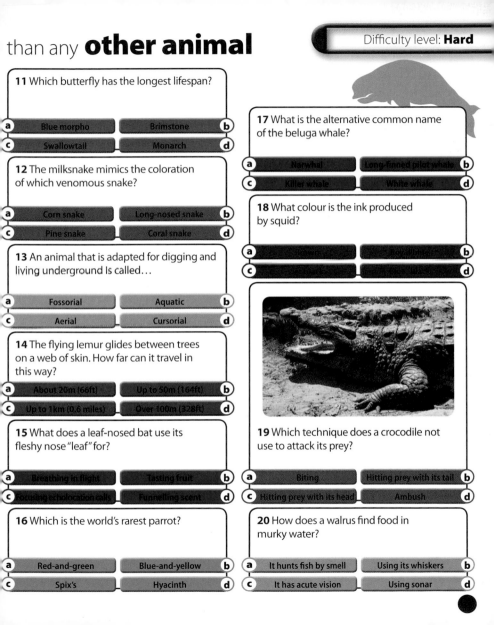

19 Which technique does a crocodile not use to attack its prey?

a Biting
b Hitting prey with its tail
c Hitting prey with its head
d Ambush

20 How does a walrus find food in murky water?

a It hunts fish by smell
b Using its whiskers
c It has acute vision
d Using sonar

Bats are the **only**

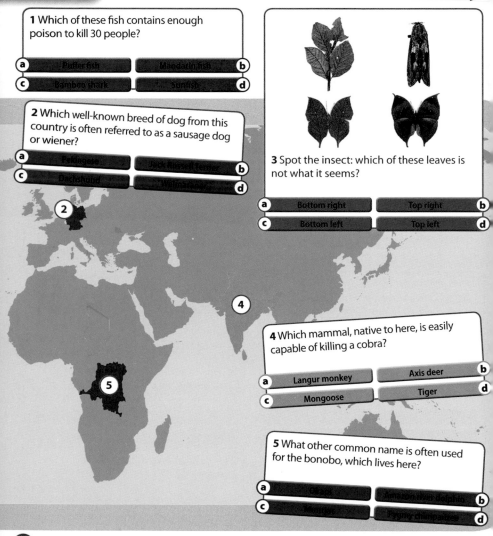

1 Which of these fish contains enough poison to kill 30 people?

a. Puffer fish
b. Mandarin fish
c. Bamboo shark
d. Sunfish

2 Which well-known breed of dog from this country is often referred to as a sausage dog or wiener?

a. Pekingese
b. Jack Russell Terrier
c. Dachshund
d. Weimaraner

3 Spot the insect: which of these leaves is not what it seems?

a. Bottom right
b. Top right
c. Bottom left
d. Top left

4 Which mammal, native to here, is easily capable of killing a cobra?

a. Langur monkey
b. Axis deer
c. Mongoose
d. Tiger

5 What other common name is often used for the bonobo, which lives here?

a. Okapi
b. Amazon river dolphin
c. Mandrill
d. Pygmy chimpanzee

mammals that can **fly**

6 To which genus do swans belong?

a. *Cygnus*
b. *Bubo*
c. *Ardea*
d. *Gavia*

7 Which is the fastest fish in the ocean?

a. Tarpon
b. Tuna
c. Swordfish
d. Sailfish

8 In which habitat would you find an American buffalo?

a. Desert
b. Rainforest
c. Mountains
d. Temperate grassland

9 Which bird is traditionally kept in the Tower of London?

a. Peregrine falcon
b. Peacock
c. Crow
d. Raven

10 What was the name of the ship in which Darwin sailed around the world?

a. *Rattlesnake*
b. *Beagle*
c. *Endeavour*
d. *Challenger*

11 Cleopatra killed herself with a bite from which type of snake?

a. Cobra
b. Taipan
c. Asp (viper)
d. Boa

12 What do you call the place where bats rest during the day?

a. Roost
b. Perch
c. Beam
d. Fortress

13 Which fly is commonly found among seaweed on the beach?

a. House fly
b. Bluebottle fly
c. Horsefly
d. Kelp fly

14 Which of these, according to the Bible, was one of the ten plagues of Egypt?

a. Beetles
b. Locusts
c. Bees
d. Ants

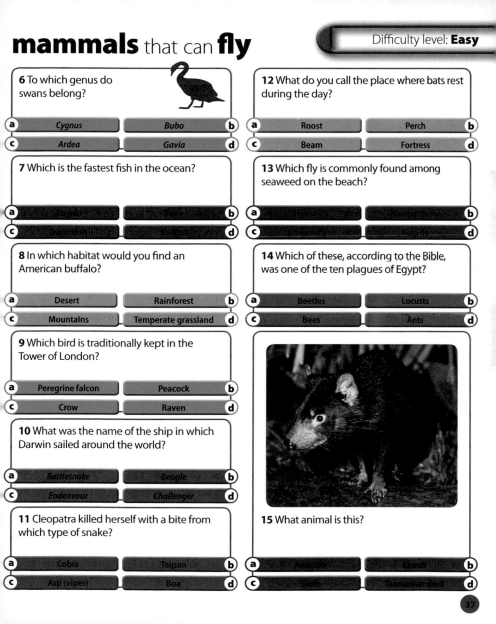

15 What animal is this?

a. Anteater
b. Lemur
c. Sloth
d. Tasmanian devil

1 The jaws of which animal deliver the most powerful bite?

a Spotted hyena **b** Wolf
c Komodo dragon **d** American alligator

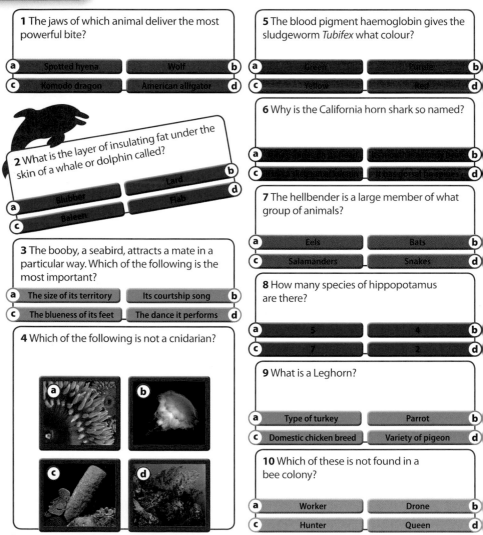

2 What is the layer of insulating fat under the skin of a whale or dolphin called?

a Blubber **b** Lard
c Baleen **d** Flab

3 The booby, a seabird, attracts a mate in a particular way. Which of the following is the most important?

a The size of its territory **b** Its courtship song
c The blueness of its feet **d** The dance it performs

4 Which of the following is not a cnidarian?

5 The blood pigment haemoglobin gives the sludgeworm *Tubifex* what colour?

a Green **b** Purple
c Yellow **d** Red

6 Why is the California horn shark so named?

a   **b**
c   **d**

7 The hellbender is a large member of what group of animals?

a Eels **b** Bats
c Salamanders **d** Snakes

8 How many species of hippopotamus are there?

a 5 **b** 4
c 7 **d** 2

9 What is a Leghorn?

a Type of turkey **b** Parrot
c Domestic chicken breed **d** Variety of pigeon

10 Which of these is not found in a bee colony?

a Worker **b** Drone
c Hunter **d** Queen

times their own **weight**

11 What is the correct term for a blood-sucking insect?

a Symbiont	**b** Partner
c Ectoparasite	**d** Endoparasite

12 Giant squid make up most of the diet of which mammal?

a Blue whale	**b** Minimal
c Sperm whale	**d** Killer whale

13 Who came up with a similar theory to Darwin, forcing him to go public in 1858?

a Samuel Wilberforce	**b** Ernst Haeckel
c Alfred Russel Wallace	**d** Richard Owen

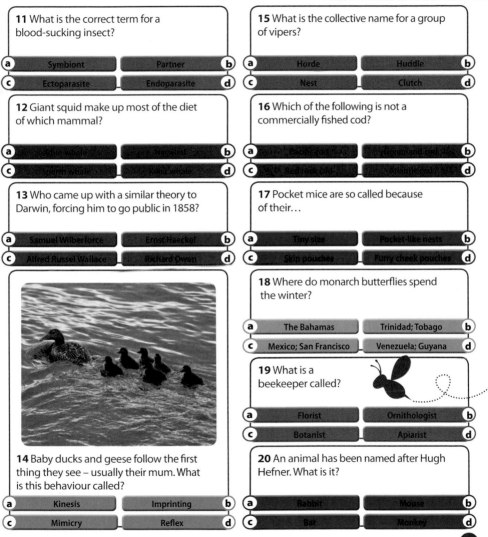

14 Baby ducks and geese follow the first thing they see – usually their mum. What is this behaviour called?

a Kinesis	**b** Imprinting
c Mimicry	**d** Reflex

15 What is the collective name for a group of vipers?

a Horde	**b** Huddle
c Nest	**d** Clutch

16 Which of the following is not a commercially fished cod?

a Pacific cod	**b** Greenland cod
c Red rock cod	**d** Atlantic cod

17 Pocket mice are so called because of their…

a Tiny size	**b** Pocket-like nests
c Skin pouches	**d** Furry cheek pouches

18 Where do monarch butterflies spend the winter?

a The Bahamas	**b** Trinidad; Tobago
c Mexico; San Francisco	**d** Venezuela; Guyana

19 What is a beekeeper called?

a Florist	**b** Ornithologist
c Botanist	**d** Apiarist

20 An animal has been named after Hugh Hefner. What is it?

a Rabbit	**b** Mouse
c Bat	**d** Monkey

A **cockroach** can **live** for

1 Which is the only part of a gazelle's carcass a hyena will not try to eat?

- **a** Hooves
- **b** Stomach contents
- **c** Horns
- **d** Teeth

2 Where do young seahorses hatch?

- **a** Floating in the plankton
- **b** In dense seaweed
- **c** In their father's pouch
- **d** Among coral reefs

3 Sixty European starlings were introduced to New York's Central Park in 1890. How many live in the US now?

- **a** None, they died out
- **b** About 1 million
- **c** About 500,000
- **d** About 200 million

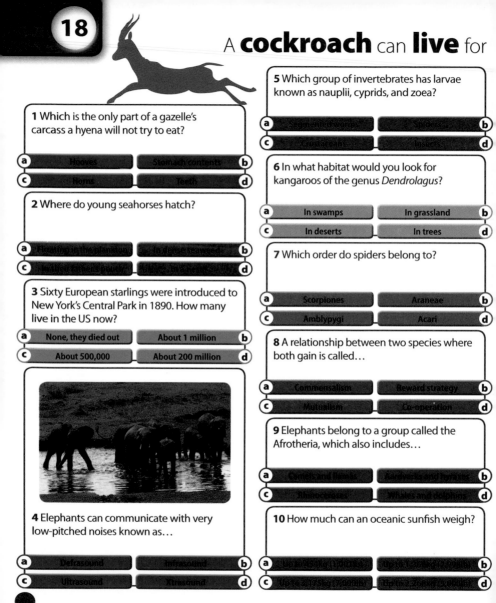

4 Elephants can communicate with very low-pitched noises known as…

- **a** Defrasound
- **b** Infrasound
- **c** Ultrasound
- **d** Xtrasound

5 Which group of invertebrates has larvae known as nauplii, cyprids, and zoea?

- **a** Segmented worms
- **b** Spiders
- **c** Crustaceans
- **d** Insects

6 In what habitat would you look for kangaroos of the genus *Dendrolagus*?

- **a** In swamps
- **b** In grassland
- **c** In deserts
- **d** In trees

7 Which order do spiders belong to?

- **a** Scorpiones
- **b** Araneae
- **c** Amblypygi
- **d** Acari

8 A relationship between two species where both gain is called…

- **a** Commensalism
- **b** Reward strategy
- **c** Mutualism
- **d** Co-operation

9 Elephants belong to a group called the Afrotheria, which also includes…

- **a** Camels and llamas
- **b** Aardvarks and hyraxes
- **c** Rhinoceroses
- **d** Whales and dolphins

10 How much can an oceanic sunfish weigh?

- **a** Up to 454kg (1,000lb)
- **b** Up to 1,361kg (3,000lb)
- **c** Up to 3,175kg (7,000lb)
- **d** Up to 2,268kg (5,000lb)

nine days without its **head**

11 A bombardier beetle defends itself from predators by…

a) Playing dead	b) Spitting blood
c) Using a noxious spray	d) Kicking up grit

12 To which group of birds does the American chickadee belong?

a) Tit family	b) Warbler family
c) Wagtail family	d) Thrush family

13 How many birds are there in a typical king penguin colony?

a) 600,000	b) 6 million
c) 60,000	d) 1 million

14 Which bird has claws on its wings?

a) Griffon vulture	b) Harpy eagle
c) Emperor penguin	d) Hoatzin

15 What is the correct name for the projections on a giraffe's head?

a) Ossicones	b) Horns
c) Antlers	d) Bony outgrowths

16 Which birds did Darwin collect in the Galapagos Islands that are collectively prefixed with his name?

a) Frigatebirds	b) Finches
c) Pelicans	d) Boobies

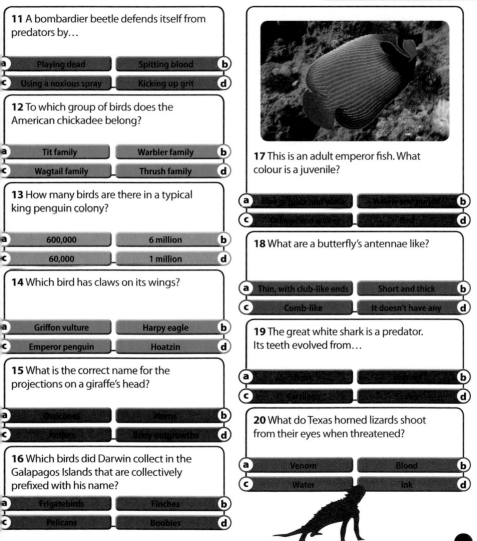

17 This is an adult emperor fish. What colour is a juvenile?

a) Blue or black and white	b) Yellow and purple
c) Orange and white	d) Red

18 What are a butterfly's antennae like?

a) Thin, with club-like ends	b) Short and thick
c) Comb-like	d) It doesn't have any

19 The great white shark is a predator. Its teeth evolved from…

a) Bone	b) Enamel
c) Cartilage	d) Scales

20 What do Texas horned lizards shoot from their eyes when threatened?

a) Venom	b) Blood
c) Water	d) Ink

Mammals are found on **land**, in

1 In the TV show *The Muppets*, what was the name of the frog?

a) Gonzo
b) Elmo
c) Cookie Monster
d) Kermit

2 A spider first senses prey trapped in its web through…

a) Vibration (touch)
b) Smell
c) Taste
d) Sight

3 The brightest coloured fish are found where?

a) Coral reefs
b) Tidal pools
c) Rivers
d) Ocean depths

4 What is another name for a lobster trap?

a) Mesh
b) Pot
c) Basket
d) Creel

5 What can a tiger, a lion, a leopard, and a jaguar do that a cheetah can't?

a) Run fast
b) Purr
c) Roar
d) Hunt

6 From which fish do we traditionally get caviar?

a) Carp
b) Tarpon
c) Sturgeon
d) Pike

7 What is stored in the hump of a camel?

a) Water
b) Baby camels
c) Partially digested grass
d) Fat

8 Roughly how many species of insects have been identified?

a) 5 million
b) About 10,000
c) About 100,000
d) More than 1 million

water, and in the **air**

9 Which animal can increase the size of its mouth to swallow large food items?

| a | Cuckoo | Clownfish | b |
| c | Snake | Mongoose | d |

10 Which of the following is a major predator of emperor penguins like these?

| a | Arctic fox | Shark | b |
| c | Leopard seal | Polar bear | d |

11 What do people generally keep in aviaries?

| a | Guinea pigs | Birds | b |
| c | Tortoises | Bees | d |

12 Lyrebirds, starlings, parrots, and mynahs have a talent in common. They can…

| a | Migrate great distances | Imitate sounds closely | b |
| c | Hang upside down | Learn sign language | d |

13 Which fish maintains a cleaning station where other fish come to have parasites removed?

| a | Climbing perch | Cleaner wrasse | b |
| c | Sabre-toothed blenny | Zebra fish | d |

14 Which type of snakes make up the family Boidae?

| a | Boas | Pipe snakes | b |
| c | Cobras | Blind snakes | d |

15 What is the name of this mammal?

| a | Bushbaby | Meerkat | b |
| c | Koala | Lemur | d |

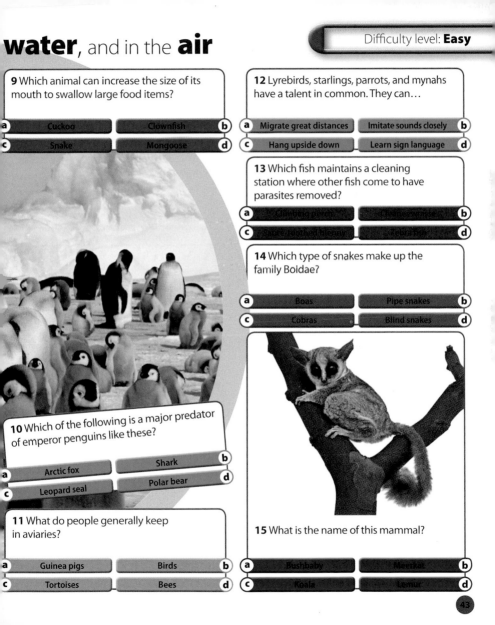

1 Which flamingo is found in S America?

a Puna
b Lesser
c Greater
d None

2 Locusts respire through tiny holes called…

a Statocysts
b Ommatidia
c Spiracles
d Ocelli

3 Which mammal can hear with its feet?

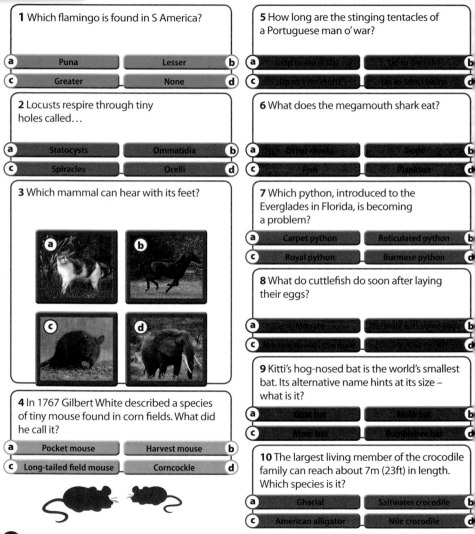

4 In 1767 Gilbert White described a species of tiny mouse found in corn fields. What did he call it?

a Pocket mouse
b Harvest mouse
c Long-tailed field mouse
d Corncockle

5 How long are the stinging tentacles of a Portuguese man o' war?

a Up to 4m (13ft)
b Up to 16m (52ft)
c Up to 17m (56ft)
d Up to 50m (160ft)

6 What does the megamouth shark eat?

a Other sharks
b Seals
c Fish
d Plankton

7 Which python, introduced to the Everglades in Florida, is becoming a problem?

a Carpet python
b Reticulated python
c Royal python
d Burmese python

8 What do cuttlefish do soon after laying their eggs?

a Migrate
b The male eats some eggs
c The female eats the male
d Die

9 Kitti's hog-nosed bat is the world's smallest bat. Its alternative name hints at its size – what is it?

a Gnat bat
b Moth bat
c Atom bat
d Bumblebee bat

10 The largest living member of the crocodile family can reach about 7m (23ft) in length. Which species is it?

a Gharial
b Saltwater crocodile
c American alligator
d Nile crocodile

11 Which land animal migrates the furthest?

a Mountain goat	b Caribou
c Wildebeest	d Saiga

12 What is the main difference between mammal horns and antlers?

a Horns don't branch	b Only males have horns
c Horns are more pointed	d Horns are permanent

13 Which molluscs are considered to be the most intelligent?

a Gastropods	b Monoplacophorans
c Cephalopods	d Bivalves

14 Where would you find the Port Jackson shark?

a S Africa	b Scandinavia
c Australia	d Hawaii

15 Which bird has such large feet that it can walk on floating water plants?

a Plover	b Jacana
c Oystercatcher	d Snipe

16 The fruit fly is one of the world's most studied animals. What sort of research is it used for?

a Agriculture	b Aeronautics
c Genetics	d Pest control

17 What do detritivores eat?

a Baby mice	b Unripe fruit
c Decaying organic matter	d Nectar

18 What is the external skeleton of an insect like a ladybird made of?

a Chitin	b Cartilage
c Bone	d Cellulose

19 Which breed of beef cattle has a deep red coat and white face?

a Hereford	b Aberdeen Angus
c Red Poll	d Sussex

20 What are feathers made of?

a Elastin	b Keratin
c Collagen	d Cellulose

1 What name is given to a group of electric eels?

(a) Shoal
(b) There is no name
(c) Swarm
(d) School

2 A hoverfly's coloration is black and yellow to mimic that of a bumblebee because…

(a) It fools its prey
(b) It deters predators
(c) It lives in beehives
(d) It supports the bees

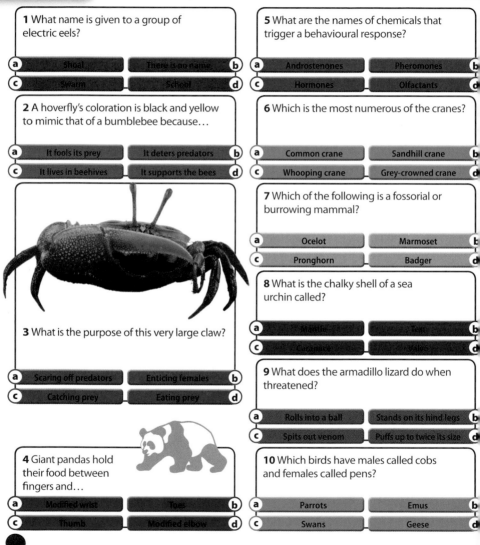

3 What is the purpose of this very large claw?

(a) Scaring off predators
(b) Enticing females
(c) Catching prey
(d) Eating prey

4 Giant pandas hold their food between fingers and…

(a) Modified wrist
(b) Toes
(c) Thumb
(d) Modified elbow

5 What are the names of chemicals that trigger a behavioural response?

(a) Androstenones
(b) Pheromones
(c) Hormones
(d) Olfactants

6 Which is the most numerous of the cranes?

(a) Common crane
(b) Sandhill crane
(c) Whooping crane
(d) Grey-crowned crane

7 Which of the following is a fossorial or burrowing mammal?

(a) Ocelot
(b) Marmoset
(c) Pronghorn
(d) Badger

8 What is the chalky shell of a sea urchin called?

(a) Mantle
(b) Test
(c) Carapace
(d) Valve

9 What does the armadillo lizard do when threatened?

(a) Rolls into a ball
(b) Stands on its hind legs
(c) Spits out venom
(d) Puffs up to twice its size

10 Which birds have males called cobs and females called pens?

(a) Parrots
(b) Emus
(c) Swans
(d) Geese

11 Which turtle feeds mainly on sponges?

a Green sea turtle | b Olive Ridley turtle
c Hawksbill | d Leatherback

12 What behaviour is shown when a fish visits a cleaner shrimp?

a Commensalism | b There is no name
c Mutualism | d Parasitism

13 What is the scientific word for the wing membrane of a bat?

a Patagium | b Web
c Marsupium | d Colostrum

14 The tawny frogmouth is a nocturnal bird with what sort of call?

a Shrill scream | b Frog-like trill
c Repetitive hoot | d Far-carrying croak

15 Who first attempted to classify animals?

a Aristotle | b Charles Darwin
c Carl Linnaeus | d John Ray

16 What do ghost knifefish use to communicate?

a Bubbles | b Colour changes
c Electrical signals | d Chemical signals

17 The largest species of seal grows to almost 7m (23ft) long. What is it?

a Leopard seal | b Crabeater seal
c Southern elephant seal | d Northern elephant seal

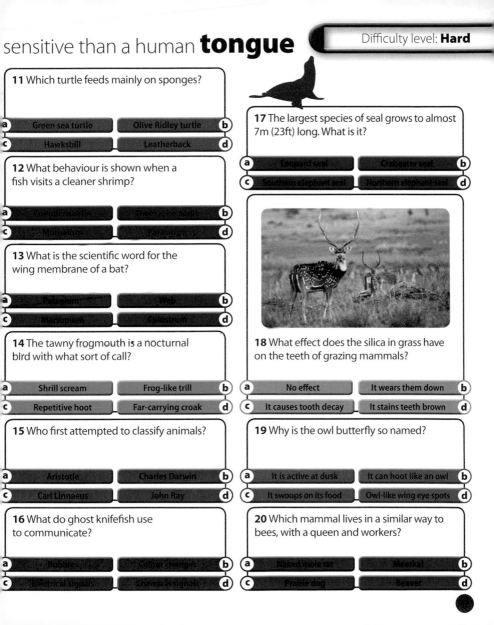

18 What effect does the silica in grass have on the teeth of grazing mammals?

a No effect | b It wears them down
c It causes tooth decay | d It stains teeth brown

19 Why is the owl butterfly so named?

a It is active at dusk | b It can hoot like an owl
c It swoops on its food | d Owl-like wing eye spots

20 Which mammal lives in a similar way to bees, with a queen and workers?

a Naked mole rat | b Meerkat
c Prairie dog | d Beaver

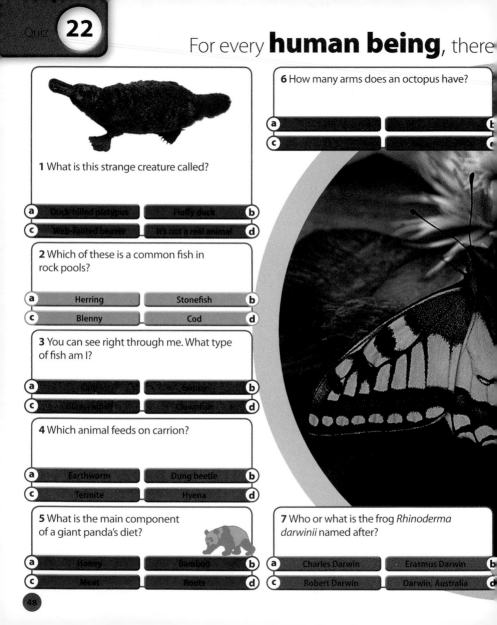

1 What is this strange creature called?

a Duck-billed platypus

b Fluffy duck

c Web-footed beaver

d It's not a real animal

2 Which of these is a common fish in rock pools?

a Herring

b Stonefish

c Blenny

d Cod

3 You can see right through me. What type of fish am I?

a Carp

b Guppy

c Glasscatfish

d Clownfish

4 Which animal feeds on carrion?

a Earthworm

b Dung beetle

c Termite

d Hyena

5 What is the main component of a giant panda's diet?

a Honey

b Bamboo

c Meat

d Roots

6 How many arms does an octopus have?

a

b

c

d

7 Who or what is the frog *Rhinoderma darwinii* named after?

a Charles Darwin

b Erasmus Darwin

c Robert Darwin

d Darwin, Australia

8 How do gibbons move through their forest habitat?

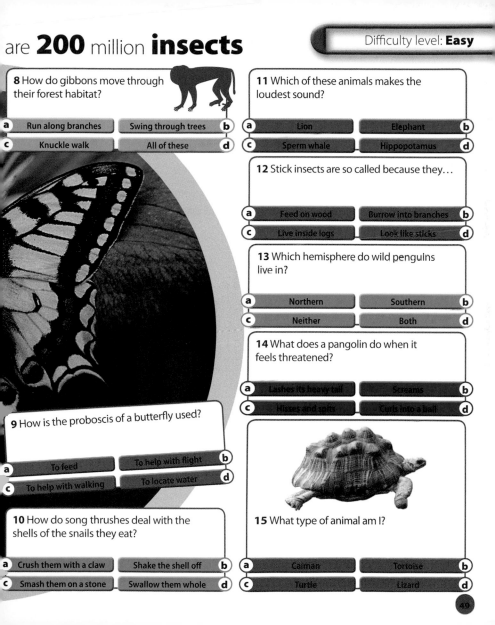

a Run along branches
b Swing through trees
c Knuckle walk
d All of these

9 How is the proboscis of a butterfly used?

a To feed
b To help with flight
c To help with walking
d To locate water

10 How do song thrushes deal with the shells of the snails they eat?

a Crush them with a claw
b Shake the shell off
c Smash them on a stone
d Swallow them whole

11 Which of these animals makes the loudest sound?

a Lion
b Elephant
c Sperm whale
d Hippopotamus

12 Stick insects are so called because they…

a Feed on wood
b Burrow into branches
c Live inside logs
d Look like sticks

13 Which hemisphere do wild penguins live in?

a Northern
b Southern
c Neither
d Both

14 What does a pangolin do when it feels threatened?

a Lashes its heavy tail
b Screams
c Hisses and spits
d Curls into a ball

15 What type of animal am I?

a Caiman
b Tortoise
c Turtle
d Lizard

49

The **collective** term for a **group**

1 What is a quetzal?

a Young llama
b Mexican bird
c Spiny mouse
d Type of bread

2 How many species of coelacanth are there?

a 20
b
c
d

3 How deep can emperor penguins dive?

a 350m (1,148ft)
b 540m (1,772ft)
c 100m (328ft)
d 250m (820ft)

4 What are scientists who study mollusc shells called?

a Beachcombers
b Conchologists
c Teuthologists
d Taxonomists

5 The world's deadliest snake produces enough venom to kill 100 people in one bite. What is it?

a Inland taipan
b Green mamba
c Coral snake
d Puff adder

6 Where can you catch a lobster?

a Pacific
b Atlantic
c Neither of these
d Both of these

7 Koalas wean their young with a special starter food called pap. What is pap?

a Extra thick milk
b Nutritious vomit
c Mother's droppings
d Chewed fruit

8 Where would you find a Gila monster?

a Europe
b N America
c Australia
d Asia

9 How do marmots survive a shortage of food in the winter? They…

a Hibernate
b Migrate
c Feed on stored food
d Forage under the snow

10 What is the collective name for a group of flies?

a Colony
b Cloud
c Cluster
d Crowd

of **frogs** is a **chorus**

11 Which is the largest toucan?

(a) Toco toucan
(b) Keel-billed toucan
(c) Red-breasted toucan
(d) Lettered aracari

12 Which of the following provides us with evidence for evolution?

(a) Genetics
(b) Embryos
(c) Fossils
(d) All of these

13 Which of the following are paired fins?

(a) Dorsal
(b) Pectoral
(c) Anal
(d) Caudal

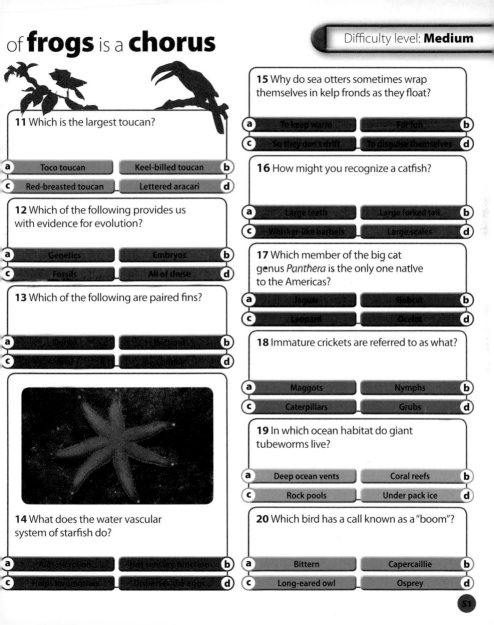

14 What does the water vascular system of starfish do?

(a) Aids excretion
(b) Has sensory function
(c) Helps locomotion
(d) Disperses the eggs

15 Why do sea otters sometimes wrap themselves in kelp fronds as they float?

(a) To keep warm
(b) For fun
(c) So they don't drift
(d) To disguise themselves

16 How might you recognize a catfish?

(a) Large teeth
(b) Large forked tail
(c) Whisker-like barbels
(d) Large scales

17 Which member of the big cat genus *Panthera* is the only one native to the Americas?

(a) Jaguar
(b) Bobcat
(c) Leopard
(d) Ocelot

18 Immature crickets are referred to as what?

(a) Maggots
(b) Nymphs
(c) Caterpillars
(d) Grubs

19 In which ocean habitat do giant tubeworms live?

(a) Deep ocean vents
(b) Coral reefs
(c) Rock pools
(d) Under pack ice

20 Which bird has a call known as a "boom"?

(a) Bittern
(b) Capercaillie
(c) Long-eared owl
(d) Osprey

A giant **anteater** can flick its **tongue**

1 Which of the following applies to all animals?

a Eukaryotic, unicellular
b Prokaryotic, multicellular
c Prokaryotic, unicellular
d Eukaryotic, multicellular

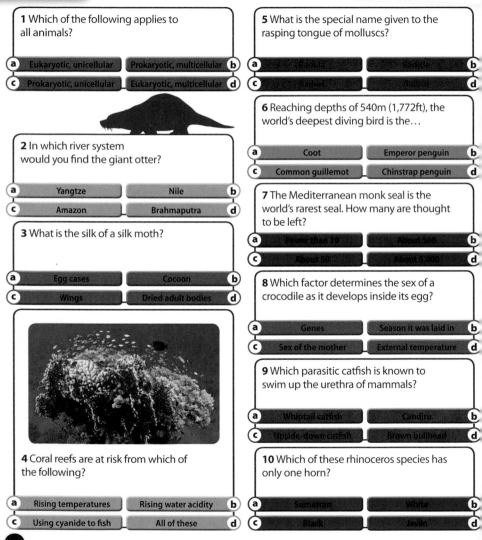

2 In which river system would you find the giant otter?

a Yangtze
b Nile
c Amazon
d Brahmaputra

3 What is the silk of a silk moth?

a Egg cases
b Cocoon
c Wings
d Dried adult bodies

4 Coral reefs are at risk from which of the following?

a Rising temperatures
b Rising water acidity
c Using cyanide to fish
d All of these

5 What is the special name given to the rasping tongue of molluscs?

a Radula
b Radide
c Radius
d Radish

6 Reaching depths of 540m (1,772ft), the world's deepest diving bird is the...

a Coot
b Emperor penguin
c Common guillemot
d Chinstrap penguin

7 The Mediterranean monk seal is the world's rarest seal. How many are thought to be left?

a Fewer than 10
b About 500
c About 50
d About 5,000

8 Which factor determines the sex of a crocodile as it develops inside its egg?

a Genes
b Season it was laid in
c Sex of the mother
d External temperature

9 Which parasitic catfish is known to swim up the urethra of mammals?

a Whiptail catfish
b Candiru
c Upside-down catfish
d Brown bullhead

10 Which of these rhinoceros species has only one horn?

a Sumatran
b White
c Black
d Javan

Difficulty level: **Hard**

11 How far can a skunk shoot foul-smelling chemicals from its anal glands?

a 10m (33ft)
b 1m (3ft)
c 20m (66ft)
d 4m (13ft)

12 What dance do honeybees perform to indicate where nectar can be found?

a Waggle dance
b Jiggle dance
c Wiggle dance
d Jingle dance

13 Which of these birds builds a mound nest?

a Duck
b Mallee fowl
c Ostrich
d Starling

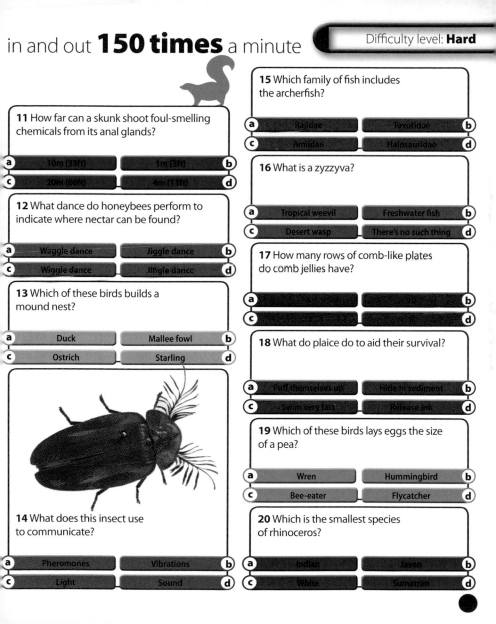

14 What does this insect use to communicate?

a Pheromones
b Vibrations
c Light
d Sound

15 Which family of fish includes the archerfish?

a Rajidae
b Toxotidae
c Amiidae
d Halosauridae

16 What is a zyzzyva?

a Tropical weevil
b Freshwater fish
c Desert wasp
d There's no such thing

17 How many rows of comb-like plates do comb jellies have?

a 6
b 70
c 12
d 8

18 What do plaice do to aid their survival?

a Puff themselves up
b Hide in sediment
c Swim very fast
d Release ink

19 Which of these birds lays eggs the size of a pea?

a Wren
b Hummingbird
c Bee-eater
d Flycatcher

20 Which is the smallest species of rhinoceros?

a Indian
b Javan
c White
d Sumatran

The **first animal** in outer **space**

1 The world's smallest mammal is a species of…

(a) Bat

(b) Mouse

(c) Guinea pig

(d) Hamster

2 Which anemone is used by some hermit crabs for camouflage?

(a) Giant anemone

(b) Jewel anemone

(c) Antarctic anemone

(d) Cloak anemone

3 Shrikes were given their alternative name of "butcher birds" because they…

(a) Live near abbatoirs

(b) Disembowel prey

(c) Peck their rivals

(d) Impale prey on thorns

4 I am a very poisonous reptile. What am I?

(a) Green turtle

(b) Fire lizard

(c) Nile crocodile

(d) Black mamba

5 What is the main function of this animal's large ears?

(a) Hearing prey

(b) Camouflage

(c) Keeping cool

(d) Hearing predators

6 Which of these freshwater fish is a top ambush predator?

(a)

(b)

(c)

(d)

7 Which animal feeds but has no gut?

(a) Tapeworm

(b) Cod

(c) Dung beetle

(d) Snail

8 Which bird appeared on the standard of Roman legions from about 104BCE?

(a) Eagle

(b) Swan

(c) Dove

(d) Raven

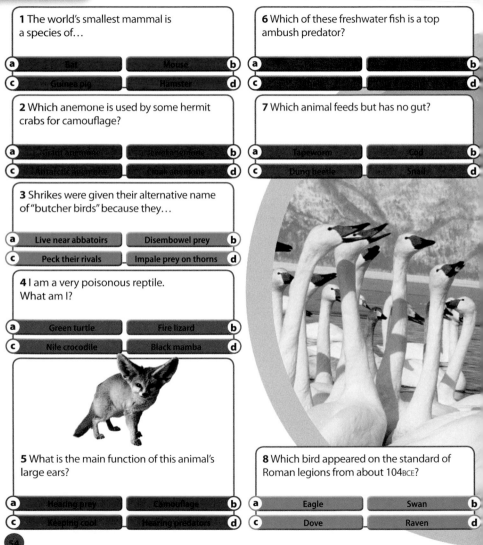

9 The blue morpho is a type of what?

- **a** Cicada
- **b** Dragonfly
- **c** Butterfly
- **d** Ant

10 Where in the world would you find a marine iguana?

- **a** Sardinia
- **b** Borneo
- **c** Galapagos Islands
- **d** Hawaii

11 What is a baby swan called?

- **a** Chick
- **b** Cygnet
- **c** Cob
- **d** Ugly duckling

12 The habitat of a dragonfly must contain plenty of what?

- **a** Sandy beaches
- **b** Grass
- **c** Water
- **d** Trees

13 How many pairs of antennae does a spider have?

- **a** 3
- **b** None
- **c** 1
- **d** 2

14 Which of these mammals lives the longest?

- **a** Rabbit
- **b** Dolphin
- **c** Chimpanzee
- **d** Cow

15 In which habitat would you find a piranha?

- **a** Sea water
- **b** Coral reef
- **c** Polar seas
- **d** Fresh water

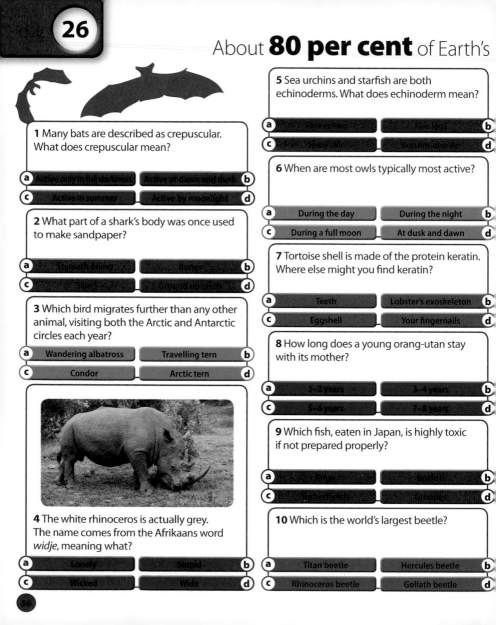

1 Many bats are described as crepuscular. What does crepuscular mean?

a Active only in full darkness | b Active at dawn and dusk
c Active in summer | d Active by moonlight

2 What part of a shark's body was once used to make sandpaper?

a Stomach lining | b Bones
c Skin | d Ground-up teeth

3 Which bird migrates further than any other animal, visiting both the Arctic and Antarctic circles each year?

a Wandering albatross | b Travelling tern
c Condor | d Arctic tern

4 The white rhinoceros is actually grey. The name comes from the Afrikaans word *widje*, meaning what?

a Lonely | b Stupid
c Wicked | d Wide

5 Sea urchins and starfish are both echinoderms. What does echinoderm mean?

a Flower-like | b Five legs
c Spiny skin | d Bottom-dweller

6 When are most owls typically most active?

a During the day | b During the night
c During a full moon | d At dusk and dawn

7 Tortoise shell is made of the protein keratin. Where else might you find keratin?

a Teeth | b Lobster's exoskeleton
c Eggshell | d Your fingernails

8 How long does a young orang-utan stay with its mother?

a 1–2 years | b 3–4 years
c 5–6 years | d 7–8 years

9 Which fish, eaten in Japan, is highly toxic if not prepared properly?

a Fugu | b Boxfish
c Butterflyfish | d Grouper

10 Which is the world's largest beetle?

a Titan beetle | b Hercules beetle
c Rhinoceros beetle | d Goliath beetle

animals are **insects**

11 Lemmings are described as subniveal animals. What does subniveal mean?

a. Suicidal
b. Scaly
c. Unsociable
d. Living under snow

12 What is it called when an animal such as a caterpillar turns into an adult butterfly?

a. Metamorphosis
b. Transmogrification
c. Crystallization
d. Adaptation

13 Scientists who study molluscs are called what?

a. Malatologists
b. Marine biologists
c. Oceanographers
d. Planktologists

14 How big is the wingspan of the Queen Alexandra's birdwing, the world's largest butterfly?

a. Up to 31cm (12in)
b. Up to 16cm (6in)
c. Up to 10cm (4in)
d. Up to 54cm (21in)

15 Which birds have recently been observed making tools?

a. Storks
b. Crows
c. Parrots
d. Owls

16 Where do albatrosses spend most of their time?

a. On the water
b. On the ground
c. In trees
d. In the air

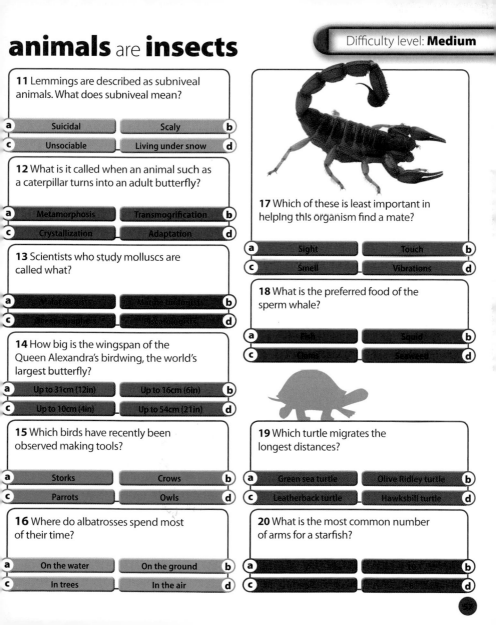

17 Which of these is least important in helping this organism find a mate?

a. Sight
b. Touch
c. Smell
d. Vibrations

18 What is the preferred food of the sperm whale?

a. Fish
b. Squid
c. Clams
d. Seaweed

19 Which turtle migrates the longest distances?

a. Green sea turtle
b. Olive Ridley turtle
c. Leatherback turtle
d. Hawksbill turtle

20 What is the most common number of arms for a starfish?

a.
b. 10
c.
d.

1 Why do opossums play dead?

a To save energy
b For peace and quiet
c To deter predators
d For fun

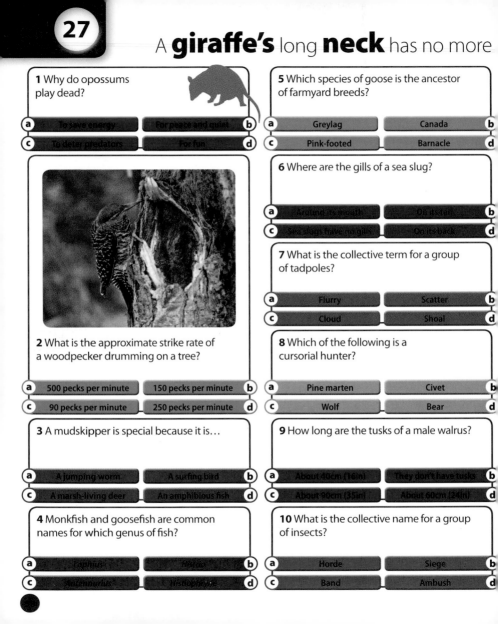

2 What is the approximate strike rate of a woodpecker drumming on a tree?

a 500 pecks per minute
b 150 pecks per minute
c 90 pecks per minute
d 250 pecks per minute

3 A mudskipper is special because it is…

a A jumping worm
b A surfing bird
c A marsh-living deer
d An amphibious fish

4 Monkfish and goosefish are common names for which genus of fish?

a Lophius
b Histrio
c Antennarius
d Histiophryne

5 Which species of goose is the ancestor of farmyard breeds?

a Greylag
b Canada
c Pink-footed
d Barnacle

6 Where are the gills of a sea slug?

a Around its mouth
b On its tail
c Sea slugs have no gills
d On its back

7 What is the collective term for a group of tadpoles?

a Flurry
b Scatter
c Cloud
d Shoal

8 Which of the following is a cursorial hunter?

a Pine marten
b Civet
c Wolf
d Bear

9 How long are the tusks of a male walrus?

a About 40cm (16in)
b They don't have tusks
c About 90cm (35in)
d About 60cm (24in)

10 What is the collective name for a group of insects?

a Horde
b Siege
c Band
d Ambush

vertebrae than a human's

11 What kind of animal is a gaur?

a Hog

b Rodent

c Ox

d Sheep

12 On which remote island can you find the endangered pink pigeon?

a Christmas Island

b Mauritius

c Hawaii

d Tristan da Cunha

13 What is a group of oysters called?

a Colony

b Bed

c Hew

d Crowd

14 Who wrote *My Family and other Animals*?

a Michael Morpurgo

b Richard Adams

c Gerald Durrell

d David Attenborough

15 What is the hard underside of a tortoise called?

a Carapace

b Plastron

c Undershell

d Lower shield

16 What do scientists count to work out how old a fish is?

a Rings in the ear bones

b Scales on the head

c Rays in the dorsal fin

d Teeth

17 Which of these animals has the most acidic conditions in its stomach?

18 All owls lay which colour eggs?

a White

b Light blue

c Brown

d Grey

19 Which of these is a strategy used by whales working together to catch fish?

a Splash herding

b Bubble netting

c Spouting

d Line fishing

20 What are the drumstick-shaped balancing organs used by flies in flight called?

a Drummers

b Bearings

c Swingers

d Halteres

The average **gestation** period of an

1 When every member of a species dies, it is said to have become what?

a Excised
b Extinct
c Erased
d Exterminated

2 How do bee-eaters avoid being stung by their prey?

a They crush it first
b They eat it headfirst
c They catch stingless bees
d They remove the sting

3 Which ray has an elongated snout?

a Stingray
b Eagle ray
c Devil ray
d Sawfish

4 Which breed of sheep is famous for its heavy fleece?

a Soay
b Merino
c Lincoln Longwool
d Southdown

5 Which part of the human body do parasitic whipworms infect?

a Ears
b Eyes
c Intestine
d Brain

6 What happens if a crab loses a leg?

a It walks with a limp
b It dies
c It grows a new one
d None of these

7 The whale's flipper is a modified…

a Fin
b Gill
c Limb
d Tail

8 Who was Edward Lear's Pussycat's travelling companion?

a Owl
b Dog
c Kingfisher
d Pig

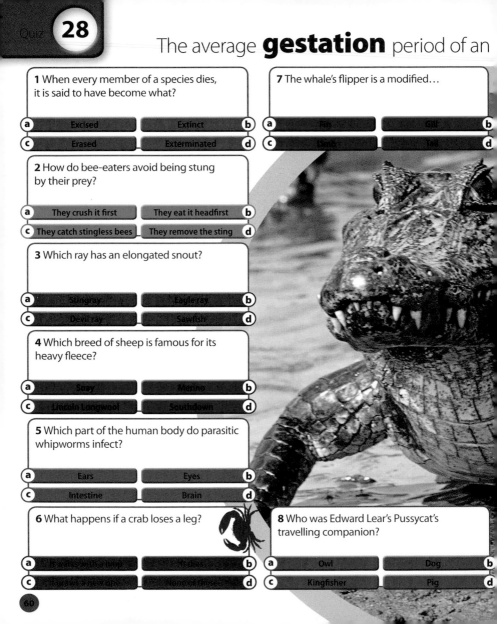

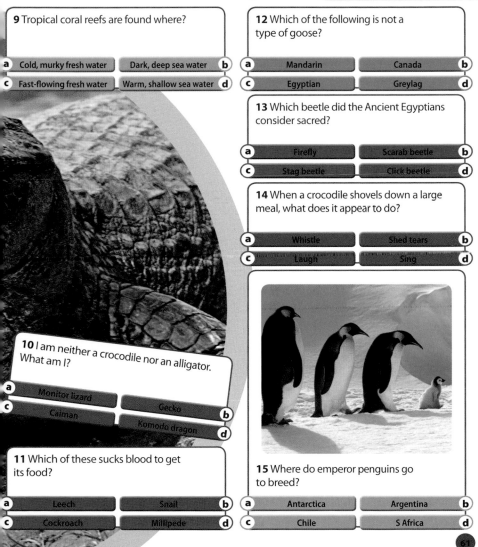

9 Tropical coral reefs are found where?

a Cold, murky fresh water
b Dark, deep sea water
c Fast-flowing fresh water
d Warm, shallow sea water

10 I am neither a crocodile nor an alligator. What am I?

a Monitor lizard
b Gecko
c Caiman
d Komodo dragon

11 Which of these sucks blood to get its food?

a Leech
b Snail
c Cockroach
d Millipede

12 Which of the following is not a type of goose?

a Mandarin
b Canada
c Egyptian
d Greylag

13 Which beetle did the Ancient Egyptians consider sacred?

a Firefly
b Scarab beetle
c Stag beetle
d Click beetle

14 When a crocodile shovels down a large meal, what does it appear to do?

a Whistle
b Shed tears
c Laugh
d Sing

15 Where do emperor penguins go to breed?

a Antarctica
b Argentina
c Chile
d S Africa

29

Male spiders sometimes get **eaten**

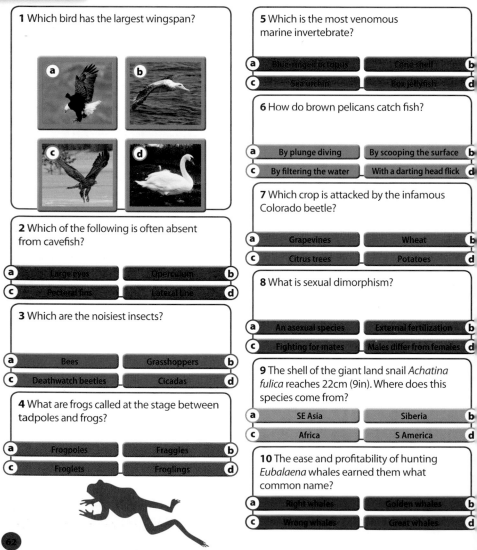

1 Which bird has the largest wingspan?

a
b
c
d

2 Which of the following is often absent from cavefish?

a Large eyes
b Operculum
c Pectoral fins
d Lateral line

3 Which are the noisiest insects?

a Bees
b Grasshoppers
c Deathwatch beetles
d Cicadas

4 What are frogs called at the stage between tadpoles and frogs?

a Frogpoles
b Fraggles
c Froglets
d Froglings

5 Which is the most venomous marine invertebrate?

a Blue-ringed octopus
b Cone shell
c Sea urchin
d Box jellyfish

6 How do brown pelicans catch fish?

a By plunge diving
b By scooping the surface
c By filtering the water
d With a darting head flick

7 Which crop is attacked by the infamous Colorado beetle?

a Grapevines
b Wheat
c Citrus trees
d Potatoes

8 What is sexual dimorphism?

a An asexual species
b External fertilization
c Fighting for mates
d Males differ from females

9 The shell of the giant land snail *Achatina fulica* reaches 22cm (9in). Where does this species come from?

a SE Asia
b Siberia
c Africa
d S America

10 The ease and profitability of hunting *Eubalaena* whales earned them what common name?

a Right whales
b Golden whales
c Wrong whales
d Great whales

11 In order to adapt, organisms must vary. How do new variations arise?

a) Inbreeding
b) Competition
c) Mutation
d) Isolation

12 What is the white fur of a newborn seal called?

a) Lanugo
b) Fleece
c) Guano
d) Colugo

13 Where are most N American lobsters caught?

a) Off Nova Scotia
b) Off Florida
c) Off British Columbia
d) Off California

14 What does a remora have on its head?

a)
b)
c)
d)

15 What colour is the breast of a male bullfinch?

a) Inky black
b) Snow white
c) Pinkish red
d) Golden yellow

16 What does a leech use to move on land?

a) Suckers
b) Teeth
c) Hydrostatic skeleton
d) Chaetae

17 Which is the largest owl?

a) Snowy owl
b) Great horned owl
c) Eurasian eagle owl
d) Pygmy owl

18 Which are scientists that study insects called?

a) Entomologists
b) Herpetologists
c) Mammalogists
d) Anthropologists

19 What anatomical feature allows squirrels to descend headfirst and hang from their back feet?

a) Prehensile tail
b) Double-jointed ankles
c) Prehensile toes
d) Backward-rotating toes

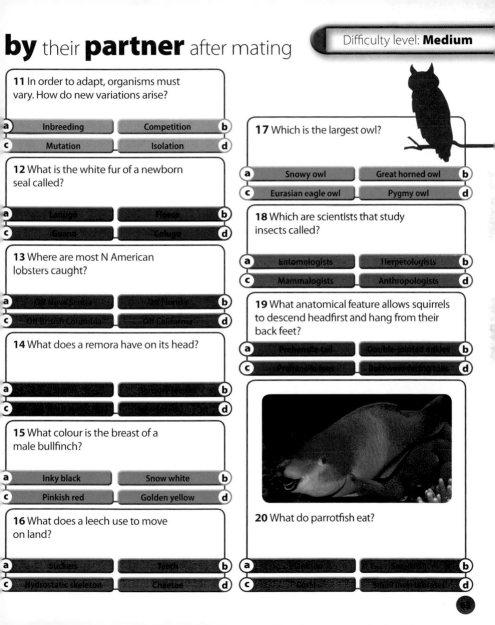

20 What do parrotfish eat?

a) Plankton
b) Seaweed
c) Coral
d) Small invertebrates

30

Owls can **turn** their heads **270°**

1 The scientific term for animals that walk with the heel of the foot touching the ground is…

- **a** Digitigrade
- **b** Bipedal
- **c** Plantigrade
- **d** Unguligrade

2 Solenodons are the large cousins of moles and shrews. On which two islands do they live?

- **a** Cuba and Hispaniola
- **b** Sumatra and Java
- **c** Hawaii and Maui
- **d** Corsica and Sardinia

3 What type of acid do ants inject when they bite?

- **a** Carbonic acid
- **b** Sulphuric acid
- **c** Formic acid
- **d** Nitric acid

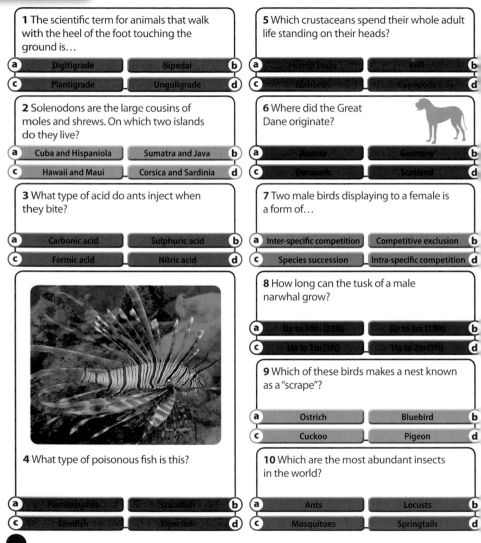

4 What type of poisonous fish is this?

- **a** Porcupine fish
- **b** Stonefish
- **c** Lionfish
- **d** Tiger fish

5 Which crustaceans spend their whole adult life standing on their heads?

- **a** Hermit crabs
- **b** Krill
- **c** Barnacles
- **d** Copepods

6 Where did the Great Dane originate?

- **a** Austria
- **b** Germany
- **c** Denmark
- **d** Scotland

7 Two male birds displaying to a female is a form of…

- **a** Inter-specific competition
- **b** Competitive exclusion
- **c** Species succession
- **d** Intra-specific competition

8 How long can the tusk of a male narwhal grow?

- **a** Up to 10m (33ft)
- **b** Up to 3m (10ft)
- **c** Up to 1m (3ft)
- **d** Up to 2m (7ft)

9 Which of these birds makes a nest known as a "scrape"?

- **a** Ostrich
- **b** Bluebird
- **c** Cuckoo
- **d** Pigeon

10 Which are the most abundant insects in the world?

- **a** Ants
- **b** Locusts
- **c** Mosquitoes
- **d** Springtails

Difficulty level: **Hard**

11 Which is the largest S American freshwater fish?

a Barramundi
b Lungfish
c Sawfish
d Arapaima

12 Which turtle grows up to 1.5m (5ft) long and weights up to 680kg (1,499lb)?

a Asian river turtle
b Leatherback turtle
c Loggerhead turtle
d Hawksbill turtle

13 The giant anteater, echidna, and pangolin have a similar appearance and diet, and are an example of what?

a Parallel evolution
b Convergent evolution
c Divergent evolution
d Radiation

14 The thresher shark uses its enormous tail to…

a Signal to other sharks
b Make noise to lure prey
c Inject venom
d Herd and stun prey

15 Why don't razorbill eggs roll off the cliff ledges where they are laid?

a They're glued with mud
b They have one flat side
c The shells are sticky
d They roll in circles

16 What kind of mammal is an aardwolf?

a Dog
b Hyena
c Anteater
d Rodent

17 What is the collective name for a group of grasshoppers?

a Plague
b Rabble
c Cackle
d Swarm

18 The Mongolian Wild Horse is named after a Russian, Nikolai Przhevalsky, who was a…

a Military explorer
b Zoologist
c Missionary
d Teacher

19 The fire salamander defends itself from attack by…

a Secreting venom
b Inflating its body
c Breathing fire
d Hissing loudly

20 What is the small fleshy fin on the back of salmon and trout called?

a Adipose fin
b Dorsal fin
c Caudal fin
d Pelvic fin

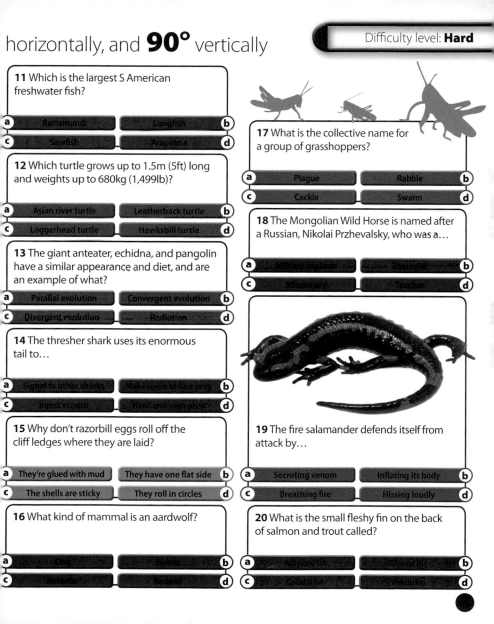

A **cricket** has an "**ear**" just **below** the

1 Which group of animals flies in a V shape?

a Flying foxes
b Flying ants
c Geese
d Bats

2 What is the flap of furry skin along a sugar glider's flanks used for?

a Parachuting
b Collecting sweet fruits
c Incubating young
d Camouflage

3 What do you call a scientist who studies fish?

a Entomologist
b Ornithologist
c Ichthyologist
d Herpetologist

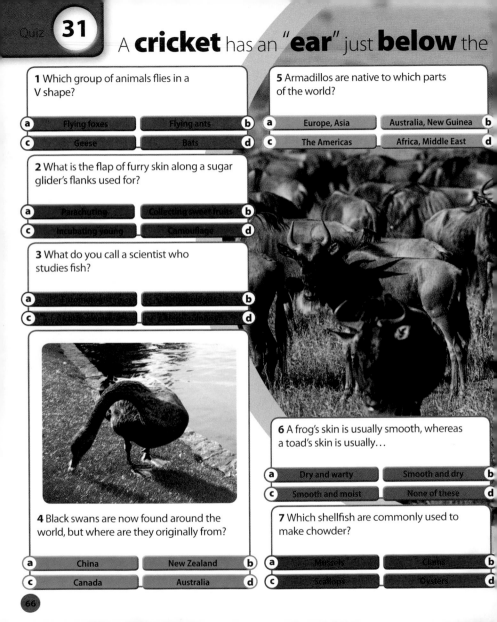

4 Black swans are now found around the world, but where are they originally from?

a China
b New Zealand
c Canada
d Australia

5 Armadillos are native to which parts of the world?

a Europe, Asia
b Australia, New Guinea
c The Americas
d Africa, Middle East

6 A frog's skin is usually smooth, whereas a toad's skin is usually…

a Dry and warty
b Smooth and dry
c Smooth and moist
d None of these

7 Which shellfish are commonly used to make chowder?

a Mussels
b Clams
c Scallops
d Oysters

8 These are wildebeest. How soon after birth can a wildebeest calf get on its feet and run?

9 What is this?

| a | Dragonfly's head | Cockroach's head | b |
| c | Bee's head | Fly's head | d |

10 Which is the largest turtle?

| a | Snapping turtle | Leatherback turtle | b |
| c | Hawksbill turtle | Green sea turtle | d |

11 Which of the following is not a type of swan?

| a | Black | Greylag | b |
| c | Mute | Trumpeter | d |

12 What does a domestic pig live in?

| a | Stable | Fold | b |
| c | Sty | Barn | d |

13 Which of these insects makes the loudest sound?

| a | Dragonfly | Wasp | b |
| c | Fly | Cricket | d |

14 In *Alice in Wonderland*, which bird was used as a croquet mallet by the Red Queen?

| a | Emu | Rhea | b |
| c | Flamingo | Ostrich | d |

15 Which terrestrial habitat contains the most animal species?

| a | Tropical rainforest | Desert | b |
| c | Taiga | Tundra | d |

Nearly **half** of all **mammal**

5 What do marine iguanas eat?

| a | Starfish | Seaweed | b |
| c | Shellfish | Anything they find | d |

1 The class Arachnida includes spiders and which other group?

| a | Centipedes | Insects | b |
| c | Scorpions | Crabs | d |

6 The feisty African ratel goes by what other common name?

| a | Hog badger | Wolverine | b |
| c | Mongoose | Honey badger | d |

2 Which turtle feeds mainly on jellyfish?

| a | Olive Ridley turtle | Leatherback turtle | b |
| c | Hawksbill turtle | Green sea turtle | d |

7 Which type of fish are sometimes referred to as living fossils?

| a | Manta rays | Coelacanths | b |
| c | Ichthyosaurs | Giant sunfish | d |

3 The colossal squid has an eye about the size of a…

| a | Beach ball | Football | b |
| c | Table tennis ball | Tennis ball | d |

8 On a bird, what is a wattle?

| a | Extra-long tail feather | Skin flap on the neck | b |
| c | Crest on the head | Colourful marking | d |

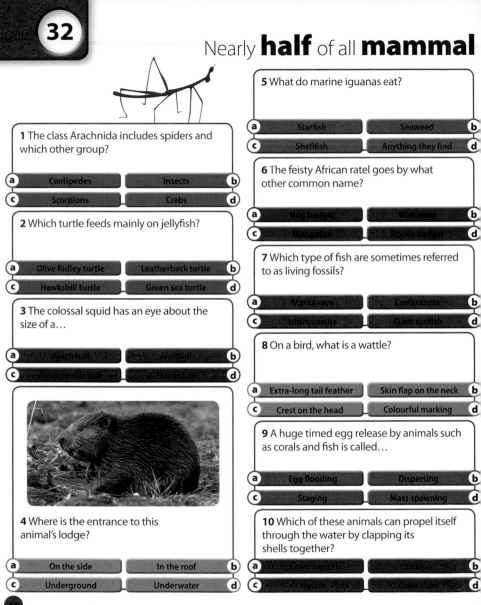

9 A huge timed egg release by animals such as corals and fish is called…

| a | Egg flooding | Dispersing | b |
| c | Staging | Mass spawning | d |

4 Where is the entrance to this animal's lodge?

| a | On the side | In the roof | b |
| c | Underground | Underwater | d |

10 Which of these animals can propel itself through the water by clapping its shells together?

| a | Swan mussel | Scallop | b |
| c | Oyster | Giant clam | d |

species are **rodents**

11 What is the burrow system of a badger called?

a Holt
b Sett
c Warren
d Latrine

12 What do stick insects eat?

a Sap
b Other insects
c Leaves
d Sticks

13 Which of the following is not an echinoderm?

a
b Sea cucumber
c Crab
d Starfish

14 Which domestic animals did Darwin study to help him understand variation?

a Pigs
b Pigeons
c Chickens
d Goats

15 Where would you find a bird's egg tooth?

a On the wings
b On top of the beak
c Inside the beak
d On the feet

16 What kind of animal is a black widow?

a Crow
b Snake
c Spider
d Toad

17 Which big cat lives only in the high mountains of Central Asia?

a Mountain lion
b Siberian tiger
c Snow leopard
d Clouded leopard

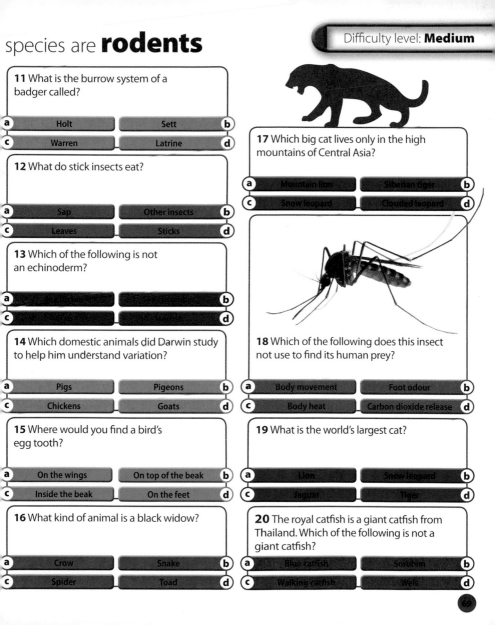

18 Which of the following does this insect not use to find its human prey?

a Body movement
b Foot odour
c Body heat
d Carbon dioxide release

19 What is the world's largest cat?

a Lion
b Snow leopard
c Jaguar
d Tiger

20 The royal catfish is a giant catfish from Thailand. Which of the following is not a giant catfish?

a Blue catfish
b Sorubim
c Walking catfish
d Wels

1 Which is the only group of crustaceans able to breed on land?

a Lobsters
b Woodlice
c Crabs
d Barnacles

2 What do you call a group of skylarks?

a Bouquet
b Choir
c Ascension
d Brood

3 What is the collective name for a group of cockroaches?

a Horde
b Cloud
c Intrusion
d Army

4 How many pure-bred Scottish wildcats remain in the wild?

a About 400
b About 4,000
c About 40
d None

5 What does a tufted duck eat?

a Fish
b Grass
c Aquatic invertebrates
d Algae

6 Which other arthropod group are horseshoe crabs most closely related to?

a Spiders
b Crustaceans
c Trilobites
d Ammonites

7 What kind of animal is a tuatara?

a Snake-like worm
b Lizard-like reptile
c Turkey-like bird
d Goat-like mammal

8 Where are the best racing camels in the world said to come from?

a Australia
b Arabia
c Egypt
d Mongolia

9 Which reptile was traditionally most hunted for tortoise shell?

a Hawksbill turtle
b Desert tortoise
c Indian starred tortoise
d Giant tortoise

10 Which of these animals has the best colour vision?

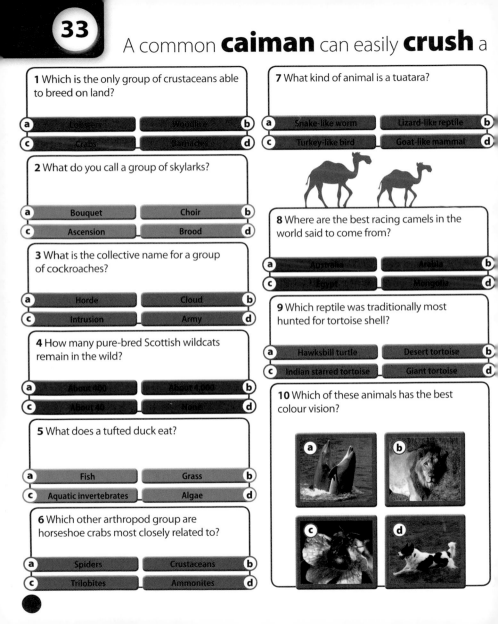

turtle shell with its mighty **jaws**

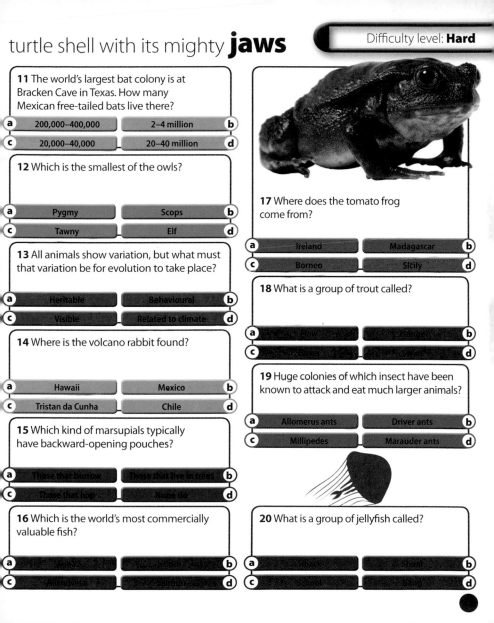

11 The world's largest bat colony is at Bracken Cave in Texas. How many Mexican free-tailed bats live there?

- **a** 200,000–400,000
- **b** 2–4 million
- **c** 20,000–40,000
- **d** 20–40 million

12 Which is the smallest of the owls?

- **a** Pygmy
- **b** Scops
- **c** Tawny
- **d** Elf

13 All animals show variation, but what must that variation be for evolution to take place?

- **a** Heritable
- **b** Behavioural
- **c** Visible
- **d** Related to climate

14 Where is the volcano rabbit found?

- **a** Hawaii
- **b** Mexico
- **c** Tristan da Cunha
- **d** Chile

15 Which kind of marsupials typically have backward-opening pouches?

- **a** Those that burrow
- **b** Those that live in trees
- **c** Those that hop
- **d** None do

16 Which is the world's most commercially valuable fish?

- **a** Tuna
- **b** Cod
- **c** Anchoveta
- **d** Salmon

17 Where does the tomato frog come from?

- **a** Ireland
- **b** Madagascar
- **c** Borneo
- **d** Sicily

18 What is a group of trout called?

- **a** Flow
- **b** Hover
- **c** Flow
- **d** Swim

19 Huge colonies of which insect have been known to attack and eat much larger animals?

- **a** Allomerus ants
- **b** Driver ants
- **c** Millipedes
- **d** Marauder ants

20 What is a group of jellyfish called?

- **a** Smack
- **b** Shoal
- **c** School
- **d** Gang

Bats make up more than

1 I have a sting in my tail and I am related to spiders. What am I?

a Scorpion **b** Ant
c Crab **d** Octopus

2 The capybara is the largest member of which group of mammals?

a Dolphins **b** Bears
c Apes **d** Rodents

3 I am a land-dwelling reptile with a shell. What am I?

a Tortoise **b** Turtle
c Horseshoe crab **d** Giant land snail

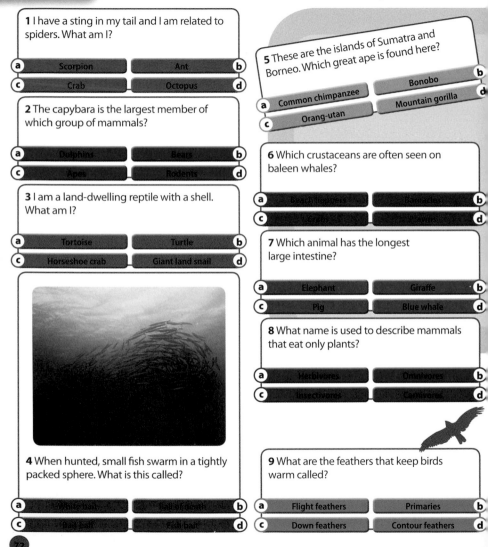

4 When hunted, small fish swarm in a tightly packed sphere. What is this called?

a White bait **b** Ball of death
c Bait ball **d** Fish bait

5 These are the islands of Sumatra and Borneo. Which great ape is found here?

a Common chimpanzee **b** Bonobo
c Orang-utan **d** Mountain gorilla

6 Which crustaceans are often seen on baleen whales?

a Beach hoppers **b** Barnacles
c Crabs **d** Prawns

7 Which animal has the longest large intestine?

a Elephant **b** Giraffe
c Pig **d** Blue whale

8 What name is used to describe mammals that eat only plants?

a Herbivores **b** Omnivores
c Insectivores **d** Carnivores

9 What are the feathers that keep birds warm called?

a Flight feathers **b** Primaries
c Down feathers **d** Contour feathers

one-fifth of mammal species

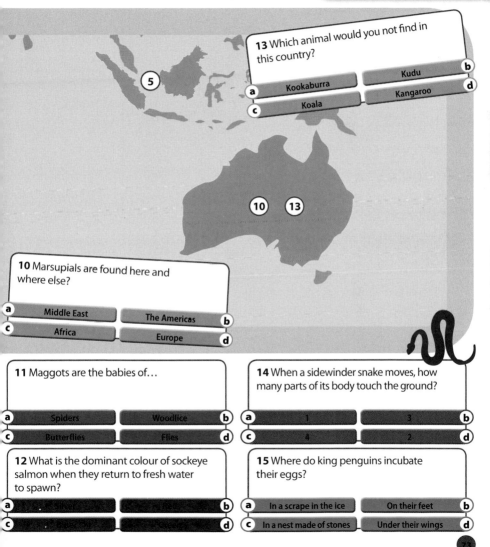

13 Which animal would you not find in this country?

a Kookaburra
b Kudu
c Koala
d Kangaroo

10 Marsupials are found here and where else?

a Middle East
b The Americas
c Africa
d Europe

11 Maggots are the babies of…

a Spiders
b Woodlice
c Butterflies
d Flies

12 What is the dominant colour of sockeye salmon when they return to fresh water to spawn?

a
b
c
d

14 When a sidewinder snake moves, how many parts of its body touch the ground?

a 1
b 3
c 4
d 2

15 Where do king penguins incubate their eggs?

a In a scrape in the ice
b On their feet
c In a nest made of stones
d Under their wings

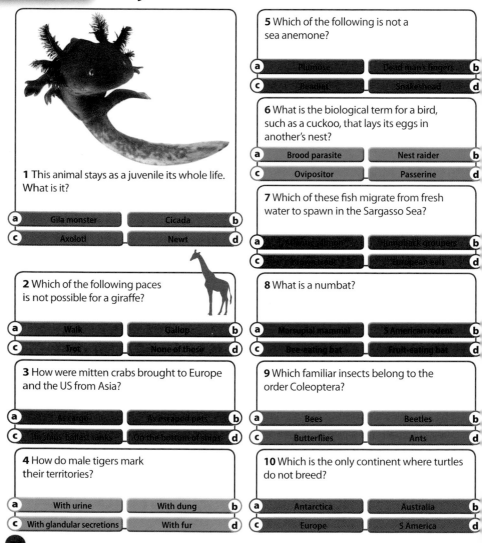

1 This animal stays as a juvenile its whole life. What is it?

a Gila monster
b Cicada
c Axolotl
d Newt

2 Which of the following paces is not possible for a giraffe?

a Walk
b Gallop
c Trot
d None of these

3 How were mitten crabs brought to Europe and the US from Asia?

a As cargo
b As escaped pets
c In ships' ballast tanks
d On the bottom of ships

4 How do male tigers mark their territories?

a With urine
b With dung
c With glandular secretions
d With fur

5 Which of the following is not a sea anemone?

a Plumose
b Dead man's fingers
c Beadlet
d Snakeshead

6 What is the biological term for a bird, such as a cuckoo, that lays its eggs in another's nest?

a Brood parasite
b Nest raider
c Ovipositor
d Passerine

7 Which of these fish migrate from fresh water to spawn in the Sargasso Sea?

a Atlantic salmon
b Humpback groupers
c Mudskippers
d European eels

8 What is a numbat?

a Marsupial mammal
b S American rodent
c Bee-eating bat
d Fruit-eating bat

9 Which familiar insects belong to the order Coleoptera?

a Bees
b Beetles
c Butterflies
d Ants

10 Which is the only continent where turtles do not breed?

a Antarctica
b Australia
c Europe
d S America

body **weight** in 30 minutes

11 Which of the following is not a trout?

- **a** Brook
- **b** Sockeye
- **c** Brown
- **d** Rainbow

12 What colour is an uncooked American lobster?

- **a** Bright red
- **b** Orange
- **c** Light brown
- **d** Dark green

13 Which bird completes this duo of Warner Brothers cartoon characters: Wile E Coyote and…?

- **a** Road Runner
- **b** Duck
- **c** Canary
- **d** Eagle

14 What kind of animal is a silverfish?

- **a** Fish
- **b** Insect
- **c** Shark
- **d** Lizard

15 Which kind of cat might be called a black panther?

- **a** Jaguar or tiger
- **b** Tiger or puma
- **c** Leopard or jaguar
- **d** Leopard or tiger

16 What is the term for an animal that lives on or in another, usually harming its host?

- **a** Parasite
- **b** Epiphyte
- **c** Passenger
- **d** Symbiont

17 About how long is the world's largest captive crocodile?

- **a** 4m (13ft)
- **b** 2m (6ft)
- **c** 8m (26ft)
- **d** 6m (20ft)

18 What are a spider's chelicerae used for?

- **a** Respiration
- **b** Feeding
- **c** Silk production
- **d** Excretion

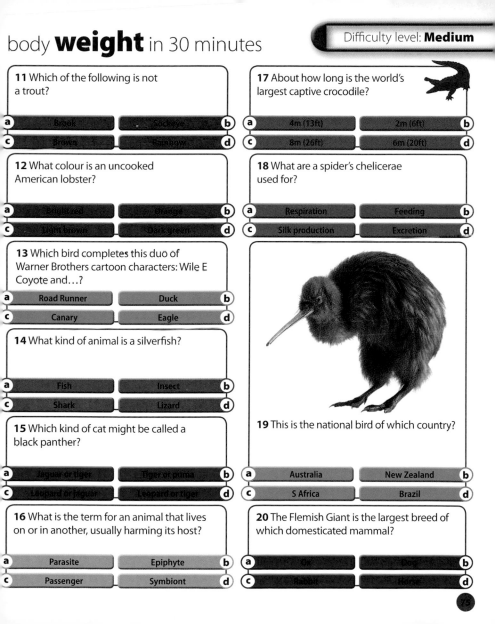

19 This is the national bird of which country?

- **a** Australia
- **b** New Zealand
- **c** S Africa
- **d** Brazil

20 The Flemish Giant is the largest breed of which domesticated mammal?

- **a** Ox
- **b** Dog
- **c** Rabbit
- **d** Horse

1 Which is the largest member of the pike family?

a Grass pickerel
b Muskellunge
c Northern pike
d Chain pickerel

2 The colour of Siamese cats is determined by what?

a Genetics
b Diet
c Age
d Temperature

3 What kind of animal is a Venus's flower basket?

a Sponge
b Coral
c Starfish
d Crab

4 Which class do springtails belong to?

a Insecta
b Arachnida
c Collembola
d Chilopoda

5 Where do the legless reptiles known as amphisbaenians normally live?

a In the sea
b In caves
c Underground
d In ponds

6 What is a matamata?

a Sideneck turtle
b Straightneck turtle
c Tortoise
d Terrapin

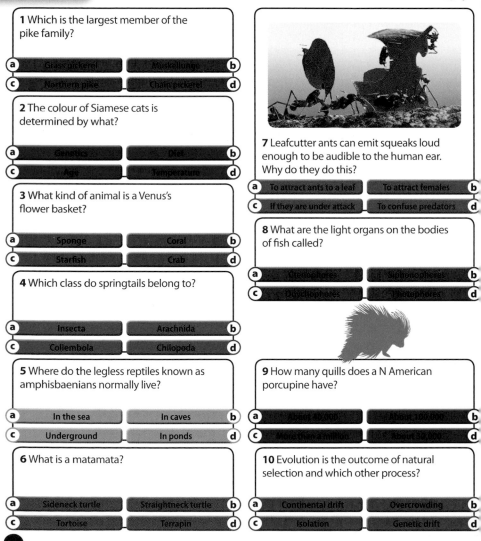

7 Leafcutter ants can emit squeaks loud enough to be audible to the human ear. Why do they do this?

a To attract ants to a leaf
b To attract females
c If they are under attack
d To confuse predators

8 What are the light organs on the bodies of fish called?

a Ctenophores
b Siphonophores
c Dactyliophores
d Photophores

9 How many quills does a N American porcupine have?

a About 40,000
b About 100,000
c More than a million
d About 30,000

10 Evolution is the outcome of natural selection and which other process?

a Continental drift
b Overcrowding
c Isolation
d Genetic drift

they stored up as **caterpillars**

11 What name is given to a roosting colony of fruit bats?

a) Hangout
b) Battery
c) Rookery
d) Camp

12 What do you call a group of goldfinches?

a) Deceit
b) Charm
c) Asylum
d) Bazaar

13 Which mollusc has an eye that is as complex as a human eye?

a) Octopus
b) Oyster
c) Giant clam
d) Whelk

14 Which of these birds does not live in a cavity nest?

a) Woodpecker
b) Hornbill
c) Parrot
d) Robin

15 Which order of insects are the highly social ants and bees?

a) Coleoptera
b) Hymenoptera
c) Lepidoptera
d) Diptera

16 There were once about 30 million bison in N America. By the late 19th century, how many were left?

a) None
b) About 10,000
c) 30 million
d) Fewer than 1,000

17 What do you call a species, like this sea otter, that plays a critical role in habitat maintenance?

a) Type species
b) Indicator species
c) Genotype
d) Keystone species

18 What is a scientist who studies snakes called?

a) Herpetologist
b) Ornithologist
c) Ophiologist
d) Apiarist

19 What is a group of budgerigars called?

a) Swoop
b) Chatter
c) Squabble
d) Comedy

20 What is the main function of a fish's swim bladder?

a) To extract oxygen
b) Buoyancy
c) Direction finder
d) Propulsion unit

Flies have **taste receptors**

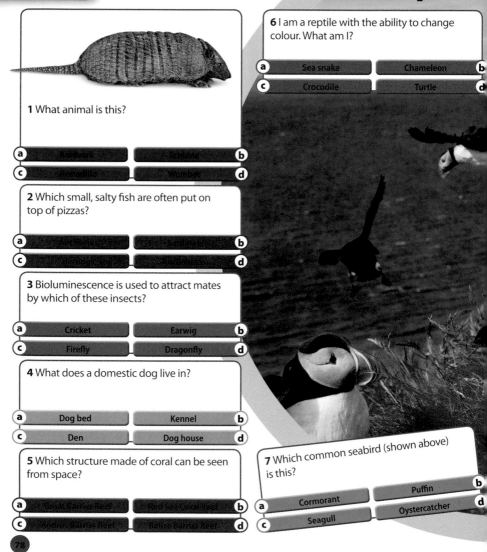

1 What animal is this?

(a) Aardvark
(b) Echidna
(c) Armadillo
(d) Wombat

2 Which small, salty fish are often put on top of pizzas?

(a) Anchovy
(b) Sardines
(c) Herring
(d) Mackerel

3 Bioluminescence is used to attract mates by which of these insects?

(a) Cricket
(b) Earwig
(c) Firefly
(d) Dragonfly

4 What does a domestic dog live in?

(a) Dog bed
(b) Kennel
(c) Den
(d) Dog house

5 Which structure made of coral can be seen from space?

(a) Great Barrier Reef
(b) Red Sea Coral Reef
(c) Andros Barrier Reef
(d) Belize Barrier Reef

6 I am a reptile with the ability to change colour. What am I?

(a) Sea snake
(b) Chameleon
(c) Crocodile
(d) Turtle

7 Which common seabird (shown above) is this?

(a) Cormorant
(b) Puffin
(c) Seagull
(d) Oystercatcher

all over their **bodies**

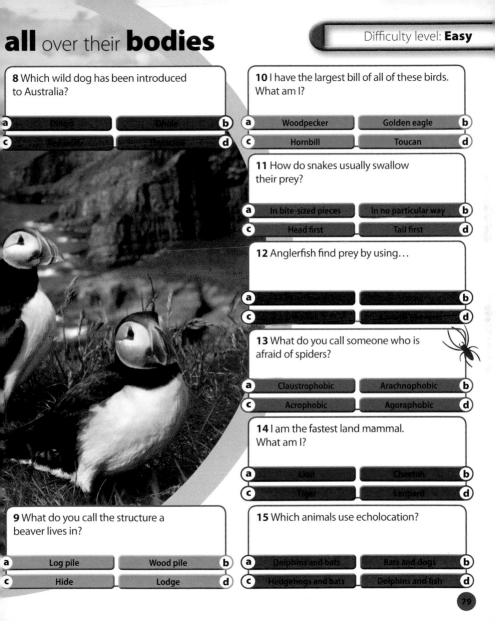

8 Which wild dog has been introduced to Australia?

a. Dingo
b. Dhole
c. Red wolf
d. Thylacine

9 What do you call the structure a beaver lives in?

a. Log pile
b. Wood pile
c. Hide
d. Lodge

10 I have the largest bill of all of these birds. What am I?

a. Woodpecker
b. Golden eagle
c. Hornbill
d. Toucan

11 How do snakes usually swallow their prey?

a. In bite-sized pieces
b. In no particular way
c. Head first
d. Tail first

12 Anglerfish find prey by using…

a.
b.
c.
d.

13 What do you call someone who is afraid of spiders?

a. Claustrophobic
b. Arachnophobic
c. Acrophobic
d. Agoraphobic

14 I am the fastest land mammal. What am I?

a. Lion
b. Cheetah
c. Tiger
d. Leopard

15 Which animals use echolocation?

a. Dolphins and bats
b. Bats and dogs
c. Hedgehogs and bats
d. Dolphins and fish

The **rougheye rockfish** can

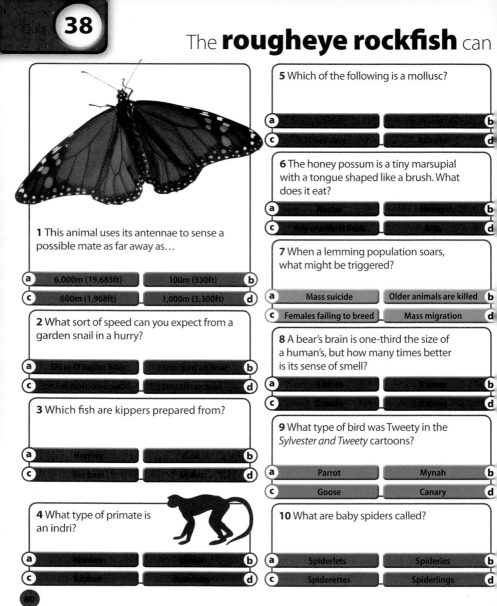

1 This animal uses its antennae to sense a possible mate as far away as…

a) 6,000m (19,685ft)
b) 100m (330ft)
c) 600m (1,968ft)
d) 1,000m (3,300ft)

2 What sort of speed can you expect from a garden snail in a hurry?

a) 58cm (23in) an hour
b) 15cm (6in) an hour
c) 5m (16ft) an hour
d) 1m (3ft) an hour

3 Which fish are kippers prepared from?

a) Herring
b) Cod
c) Sea bass
d) Mullet

4 What type of primate is an indri?

a) Monkey
b) Lemur
c) Gibbon
d) Bushbaby

5 Which of the following is a mollusc?

a) Starfish
b) Coral
c) Sea slug
d) Abalone

6 The honey possum is a tiny marsupial with a tongue shaped like a brush. What does it eat?

a) Nectar
b) Honey
c) Any crumbs it finds
d) Ants

7 When a lemming population soars, what might be triggered?

a) Mass suicide
b) Older animals are killed
c) Females failing to breed
d) Mass migration

8 A bear's brain is one-third the size of a human's, but how many times better is its sense of smell?

a) 4 times
b) 5 times
c) 2 times
d) 7 times

9 What type of bird was Tweety in the *Sylvester and Tweety* cartoons?

a) Parrot
b) Mynah
c) Goose
d) Canary

10 What are baby spiders called?

a) Spiderlets
b) Spideries
c) Spiderettes
d) Spiderlings

11 Which of these sharks swims the fastest?

a Nurse shark
b Mako shark
c Great white shark
d Leopard shark

12 Which kind of bird is an avocet?

a Stork
b Heron
c Songbird
d Wader

13 What kind of animal is a slow worm?

a Lizard
b Insect larva
c Eel
d Ribbon worm

14 Which of the following is not a rattlesnake?

a Gabon
b Diamondback
c Prairie
d Western

15 What special name is given to an otter's den?

a Warren
b Holt
c Stop
d Sett

16 Which of the following is not a coral?

a Blue button
b Brain
c Mushroom
d Table

17 What food is given to the caterpillars of a silk moth in silk farms?

a Mulberry leaves
b Nettle leaves
c Tea leaves
d Aspidistra leaves

18 What is the rattle on the tail of a rattlesnake made of?

a Small bones
b Small stones
c Cartilage
d Old scales

19 The heaviest invertebrate ever recorded was a mollusc weighing 495kg (1,100lb). Which species was it?

a Colossal squid
b Giant clam
c Giant land snail
d Sea slug

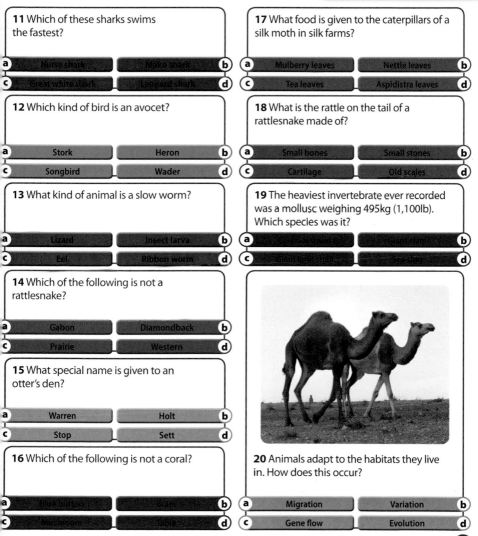

20 Animals adapt to the habitats they live in. How does this occur?

a Migration
b Variation
c Gene flow
d Evolution

Baby elephants don't leave their

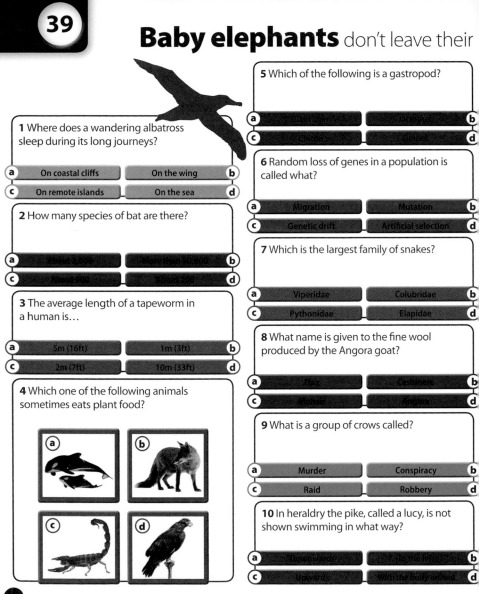

1 Where does a wandering albatross sleep during its long journeys?

a On coastal cliffs
b On the wing
c On remote islands
d On the sea

2 How many species of bat are there?

a About 3,000
b More than 50,000
c About 900
d About 200

3 The average length of a tapeworm in a human is…

a 5m (16ft)
b 1m (3ft)
c 2m (7ft)
d 10m (33ft)

4 Which one of the following animals sometimes eats plant food?

a
b
c
d

5 Which of the following is a gastropod?

a Giant clam
b Octopus
c Chiton
d Limpet

6 Random loss of genes in a population is called what?

a Migration
b Mutation
c Genetic drift
d Artificial selection

7 Which is the largest family of snakes?

a Viperidae
b Colubridae
c Pythonidae
d Elapidae

8 What name is given to the fine wool produced by the Angora goat?

a Flax
b Cashmere
c Mohair
d Angora

9 What is a group of crows called?

a Murder
b Conspiracy
c Raid
d Robbery

10 In heraldry the pike, called a lucy, is not shown swimming in what way?

a Downwards
b To the left
c Upwards
d With the body arched

mother for **eight years**

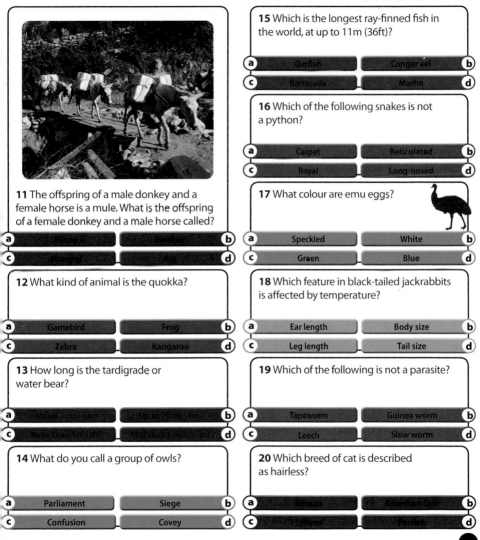

11 The offspring of a male donkey and a female horse is a mule. What is the offspring of a female donkey and a male horse called?

a	Jenny	Honker	**b**
c	Moogoo	Ass	**d**

12 What kind of animal is the quokka?

a	Gamebird	Frog	**b**
c	Zebra	Kangaroo	**d**

13 How long is the tardigrade or water bear?

a	About 1cm (½in)	Up to 10cm (4in)	**b**
c	More than 1m (3ft)	Less than 1mm (1/25in)	**d**

14 What do you call a group of owls?

a	Parliament	Siege	**b**
c	Confusion	Covey	**d**

15 Which is the longest ray-finned fish in the world, at up to 11m (36ft)?

a	Oarfish	Conger eel	**b**
c	Barracuda	Marlin	**d**

16 Which of the following snakes is not a python?

a	Carpet	Reticulated	**b**
c	Royal	Long-nosed	**d**

17 What colour are emu eggs?

a	Speckled	White	**b**
c	Green	Blue	**d**

18 Which feature in black-tailed jackrabbits is affected by temperature?

a	Ear length	Body size	**b**
c	Leg length	Tail size	**d**

19 Which of the following is not a parasite?

a	Tapeworm	Guinea worm	**b**
c	Leech	Slow worm	**d**

20 Which breed of cat is described as hairless?

a	Birman	American Curl	**b**
c	Sphynx	Persian	**d**

Arabian camels can go for

1 What am I?

a Aardvark
b Elephant shrew
c Giant anteater
d Armadillo

2 What do the spinnerets of a spider produce?

a Eggs
b Silk
c Urine
d Nothing

3 Why do hippopotamuses wallow in mud?

a To cool off
b For camouflage
c To soften their skin
d To hide their smell

4 What is a barn swallow's nest made of?

a Spit
b Feathers
c Straw
d Mud

5 I borrow old, disused shells to live in. What am I?

a Hermit crab
b Cockle
c Sea urchin
d Shrimp

6 What are antennae used for?

a Fighting
b Smelling and touching
c Seeing and hearing
d Releasing poison

7 I am a bird that likes to laugh a lot. What am I?

a Kingfisher
b Woodpecker
c Bird of paradise
d Kookabura

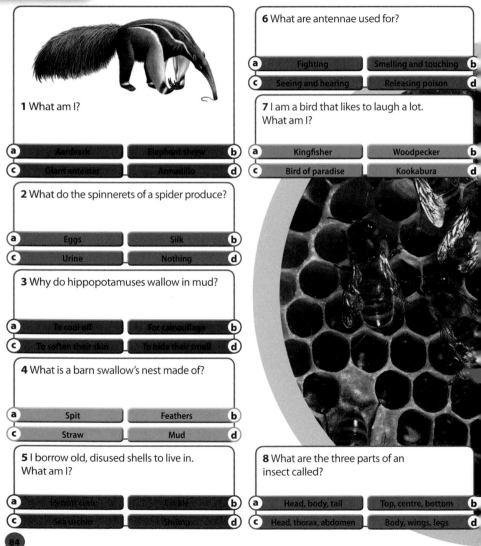

8 What are the three parts of an insect called?

a Head, body, tail
b Top, centre, bottom
c Head, thorax, abdomen
d Body, wings, legs

months without **drinking**

9 What makes lemmings move down from high ground?

a Temperature	Lack of food b
c Breeding instinct	Light intensity d

10 Most bees in a colony are what?

	Drones b
a Queens	Workers d
c Soldiers	

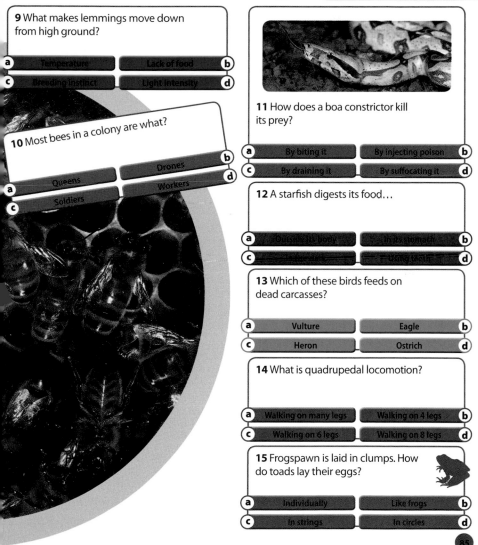

11 How does a boa constrictor kill its prey?

a By biting it	By injecting poison b
c By draining it	By suffocating it d

12 A starfish digests its food…

a Outside its body	In its stomach b
c	Using teeth d

13 Which of these birds feeds on dead carcasses?

a Vulture	Eagle b
c Heron	Ostrich d

14 What is quadrupedal locomotion?

a Walking on many legs	Walking on 4 legs b
c Walking on 6 legs	Walking on 8 legs d

15 Frogspawn is laid in clumps. How do toads lay their eggs?

a Individually	Like frogs b
c In strings	In circles d

Darwin's frog carries its

1 What term describes an animal that is genetically identical to its parent?

- (a) Offspring
- (b) Hermaphrodite
- (c) Mitosis
- (d) Clone

2 Which of the following worms lives on hydrothermal vents?

- (a) [illegible]
- (b) [illegible]
- (c) Christmas tree worm
- (d) Pompeii worm

3 What special name is given to the caste of ants that defend their colony?

- (a) Kamikaze ants
- (b) Army ants
- (c) Soldier ants
- (d) Fire ants

4 What is a male honeybee called?

- (a) Soldier
- (b) Worker
- (c) King
- (d) Drone

5 Which fins in a bony fish are used for manoeuvring?

- (a) Pelvic
- (b) Caudal
- (c) Dorsal
- (d) Pectoral

6 Which large American bird of prey has recently been reintroduced to the wild?

- (a) Turkey vulture
- (b) Northern harrier
- (c) Californian condor
- (d) Golden eagle

7 Crocodiles and alligators sometimes rest with their mouth open, because they are…

- (a) Panting after exercise
- (b) Tasting the air for prey
- (c) Trying to cool off
- (d) Hoping prey will walk in

8 Which of these are not used by animals for respiration?

- (a) Lungs
- (b) Skin
- (c) Kidneys
- (d) Gills

9 Where on the arm of a starfish are its eyespots?

- (a) Side
- (b) Base
- (c) Tip
- (d) Middle

10 Which of the following is not a type of coonhound?

- (a) Bluetick
- (b) Redbone
- (c) Treeing Walker
- (d) Irish

young in its **vocal sac**

11 What name is given to a group of tuna?

- **a** Shoal
- **b** Team
- **c** Pod
- **d** School

12 Which big cat has been known to eat turtles?

- **a** Jaguar
- **b** Tiger
- **c** Clouded leopard
- **d** Asiatic lion

13 Where are a spider's spinnerets located?

- **a** Ends of its feet
- **b** Behind its eyes
- **c** In its mouth
- **d** Back of its abdomen

14 What do these flightless birds use their wings for, if not for flying?

- **a** To fan themselves
- **b** Courtship displays
- **c** Defence
- **d** To cover their eyes

15 Which amphibian, introduced to Australia to control pest insects, became a pest itself?

- **a** African bullfrog
- **b** Fire salamander
- **c** Cane toad
- **d** Edible frog

16 Which type of bird is the laughing kookaburra?

- **a** Parrot
- **b** Seabird
- **c** Kingfisher
- **d** Crow

17 In which cacti do elf owls sometimes make their nests?

- **a** Barrel
- **b** Yucca
- **c** Saguaro
- **d** Prickly pear

18 The mammal with the best sense of touch is the…

- **a** Star-nosed mole
- **b** Meerkat
- **c** Giraffe
- **d** Mountain gorilla

19 Lonesome George is which type of reptile?

- **a** Komodo dragon
- **b** Green anaconda
- **c** Giant tortoise
- **d** Saltwater crocodile

20 Which of the following is not a salmon?

- **a** Sockeye
- **b** Coho
- **c** Rainbow
- **d** Chinook

Kingfishers' **eyes** can **filter** out **glare**

1 How do egg-eating snakes break the eggs they swallow?

- (a) With their teeth
- (b) By constriction
- (c) By dissolving the shell
- (d) With spines in the neck

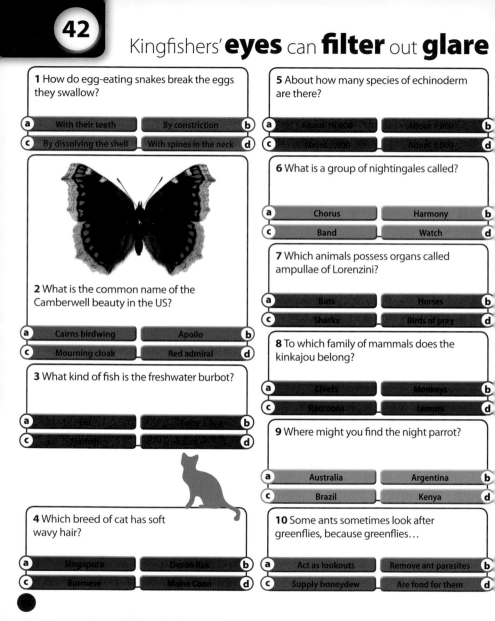

2 What is the common name of the Camberwell beauty in the US?

- (a) Cairns birdwing
- (b) Apollo
- (c) Mourning cloak
- (d) Red admiral

3 What kind of fish is the freshwater burbot?

- (a) Eel
- (b) Goby
- (c) Flatfish
- (d) Cod

4 Which breed of cat has soft wavy hair?

- (a) Singapura
- (b) Devon Rex
- (c) Burmese
- (d) Maine Coon

5 About how many species of echinoderm are there?

- (a) About 10,000
- (b) About 7,000
- (c) About 1,000
- (d) About 5,000

6 What is a group of nightingales called?

- (a) Chorus
- (b) Harmony
- (c) Band
- (d) Watch

7 Which animals possess organs called ampullae of Lorenzini?

- (a) Bats
- (b) Horses
- (c) Sharks
- (d) Birds of prey

8 To which family of mammals does the kinkajou belong?

- (a) Civets
- (b) Monkeys
- (c) Raccoons
- (d) Lemurs

9 Where might you find the night parrot?

- (a) Australia
- (b) Argentina
- (c) Brazil
- (d) Kenya

10 Some ants sometimes look after greenflies, because greenflies…

- (a) Act as lookouts
- (b) Remove ant parasites
- (c) Supply honeydew
- (d) Are food for them

from the water's **surface**

11 Complete this sentence: evolution is the _____ of natural selection.

a) Aim
b) Outcome
c) Mechanism
d) Process

12 How many toes does a horse have on each foot?

a) 3
b) 1
c) None
d) 2

13 What do you call a group of swallows?

a) Gaggle
b) Fall
c) Brood
d) Gulp

14 What substance in the brain aids navigation in some migratory animals?

a) Calcium
b) Haemoglobin
c) Magnetite
d) Melanin

15 Which of the following lizards has no legs?

a) Glass lizard
b) Green anole
c) Collared lizard
d) Ocellated skink

16 Which lungfish can survive long periods out of water by enclosing itself in a mucus-filled cocoon?

a) Australian lungfish
b) American lungfish
c) W African lungfish
d) All of them

17 What is the collective name for a group of fleas?

a) Cloud
b) Cluster
c) Flock
d) Hatch

18 Where does the Sardine Run occur?

a) Off S America
b) Off S Australia
c) In the Southern Ocean
d) Off S Africa

19 Most mammals have seven bones in their neck. A giraffe has how many?

a) 21
b) 100
c) 7
d) 12

20 How many species of mollusc are there?

a) More than 27,000
b) More than 70,000
c) More than 110,000
d) More than 15,000

An **ostrich's eyeball** is

1 I like to eat pretty much anything I can find. What am I?

a Insectivore
b Omnivore
c Bird
d Marsupial

2 Why is the puff adder so named?

a It puffs to attract a mate
b It puffs while eating prey
c It puffs up if disturbed
d It gets breathless easily

3 What do you call a scientist who studies birds?

a Conchologist
b Ornithologist
c Entomologist
d Ichthyologist

4 I am an arachnid. What could I be?

a Frog
b Spider
c Crab
d Insect

5 Animals that are camouflaged do what?

a Obtain more mates
b Blend in with a habitat
c Become conspicuous
d Gain more territory

6 Which famous palomino horse was ridden by the cowboy actor Roy Rogers?

a Silver
b Trigger
c Champion
d Topper

7 Which of these is an insect?

a Woodlouse
b Spider
c Ant
d Earthworm

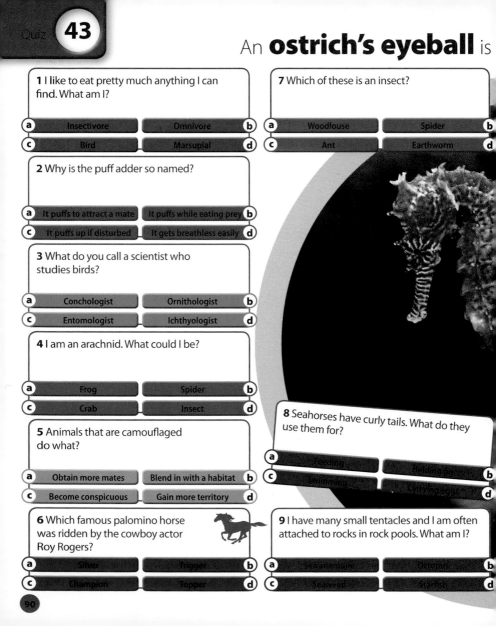

8 Seahorses have curly tails. What do they use them for?

a Feeding
b Holding on
c Swimming
d Carrying eggs

9 I have many small tentacles and I am often attached to rocks in rock pools. What am I?

a Sea anemone
b Octopus
c Seaweed
d Starfish

bigger than its **brain**

10 Which of these is the loudest land mammal?

a. Elephant
b. Lion
c. Hyena
d. Howler monkey

11 In which of these species does the male incubate the eggs?

a. Seahorse
b. Eel
c. Lemon shark
d. Triggerfish

12 What are these ants doing?

a. Attacking the bugs
b. Being attacked
c. Feeding the bugs
d. Farming the bugs

13 In a food chain, which of these is a top predator?

a. Herring
b. Salmon
c. Killer whale
d. Zooplankton

14 Which vertebrates are best suited for desert living?

a. Reptiles
b. Amphibians
c. Fish
d. Mammals

15 Which bird is referred to in this well-known saying: "As dead as a…"

a. Dodo
b. *Archaeopteryx*
c. Parrot
d. Duck

1 Which of these has the greatest number of different types of colour receptor in its eyes?

a) Bird
b) Bull
c) Human
d) Mantis shrimp

2 Which side do flatfish lie on?

a) Left
b) Top
c) Right
d) Varies between species

3 The robber crab is also known by another name, reflecting its favourite food. What is it?

a) Coral crab
b) Anemone crab
c) Mango crab
d) Coconut crab

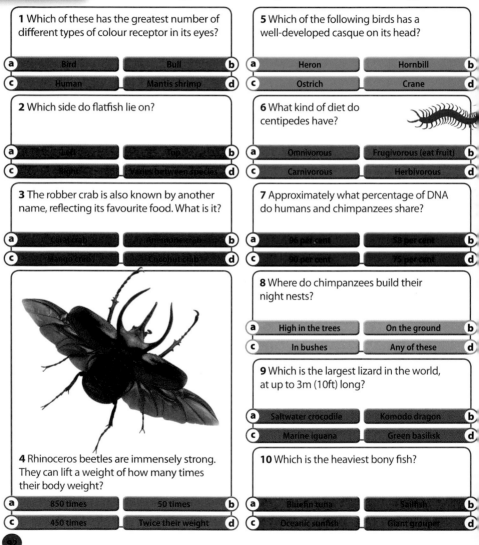

4 Rhinoceros beetles are immensely strong. They can lift a weight of how many times their body weight?

a) 850 times
b) 50 times
c) 450 times
d) Twice their weight

5 Which of the following birds has a well-developed casque on its head?

a) Heron
b) Hornbill
c) Ostrich
d) Crane

6 What kind of diet do centipedes have?

a) Omnivorous
b) Frugivorous (eat fruit)
c) Carnivorous
d) Herbivorous

7 Approximately what percentage of DNA do humans and chimpanzees share?

a) 96 per cent
b) 58 per cent
c) 90 per cent
d) 75 per cent

8 Where do chimpanzees build their night nests?

a) High in the trees
b) On the ground
c) In bushes
d) Any of these

9 Which is the largest lizard in the world, at up to 3m (10ft) long?

a) Saltwater crocodile
b) Komodo dragon
c) Marine iguana
d) Green basilisk

10 Which is the heaviest bony fish?

a) Bluefin tuna
b) Sailfish
c) Oceanic sunfish
d) Giant grouper

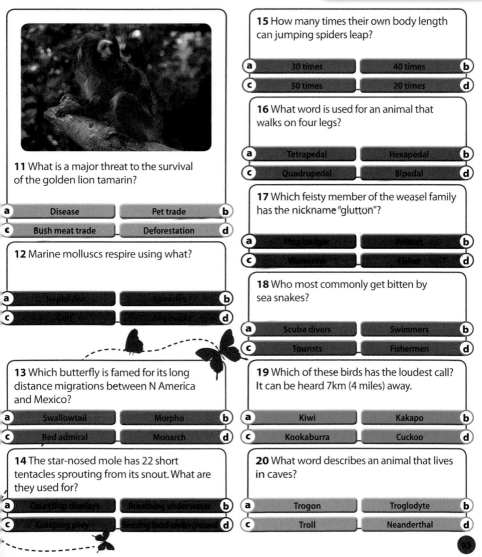

11 What is a major threat to the survival of the golden lion tamarin?

a Disease
b Pet trade
c Bush meat trade
d Deforestation

12 Marine molluscs respire using what?

a Nephridia
b Spiracles
c Gills
d Lung Books

13 Which butterfly is famed for its long distance migrations between N America and Mexico?

a Swallowtail
b Morpho
c Red admiral
d Monarch

14 The star-nosed mole has 22 short tentacles sprouting from its snout. What are they used for?

a Courtship displays
b Breathing underwater
c Grasping prey
d Sensing food underground

15 How many times their own body length can jumping spiders leap?

a 30 times
b 40 times
c 50 times
d 20 times

16 What word is used for an animal that walks on four legs?

a Tetrapedal
b Hexapedal
c Quadrupedal
d Bipedal

17 Which feisty member of the weasel family has the nickname "glutton"?

a Hog badger
b Polecat
c Wolverine
d Fisher

18 Who most commonly get bitten by sea snakes?

a Scuba divers
b Swimmers
c Tourists
d Fishermen

19 Which of these birds has the loudest call? It can be heard 7km (4 miles) away.

a Kiwi
b Kakapo
c Kookaburra
d Cuckoo

20 What word describes an animal that lives in caves?

a Trogon
b Troglodyte
c Troll
d Neanderthal

1 Which of these animals has unguligrade locomotion?

a
b
c
d

2 Which insects belong to the order Odonata?

a Dung beetles
b Dragonflies
c House flies
d Mosquitoes

3 What is a male turkey called?

a Ben
b Harry
c Tom
d Jim

4 How long does it take for a baby elephant to develop inside its mother?

a 22 months
b 12 months
c 18 months
d 7 months

5 Which of the following is not a bivalve mollusc?

a Mussel
b Tusk shell
c Oyster
d Scallop

6 Which of these ibises is found in S America?

a Northern bald
b Crested
c Scarlet
d Sacred

7 Which of the following is a venomous snake?

a Grass snake
b Leopard snake
c Boomslang
d Common kingsnake

8 What shape are the pupils in the eyes of big cats?

a Vertical slits
b Round
c Oval
d Horizontal slits

9 What happens when a male bluehead wrasse dies?

a Females move away
b Breeding stops
c A female becomes male
d Another male arrives

10 How might a hydra move?

a Loops
b Glides
c Somersaults
d All of these

its feet, so it can **walk** on **ice**

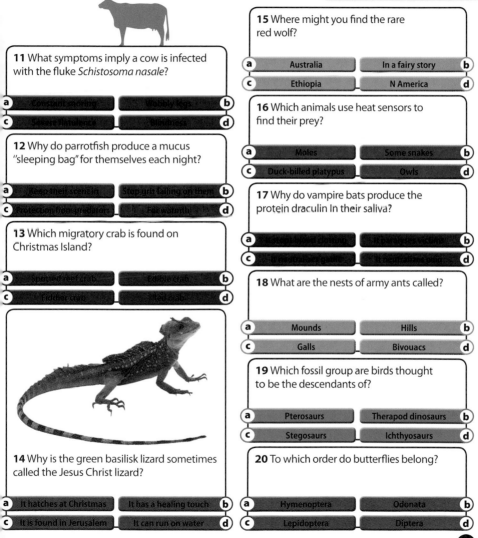

11 What symptoms imply a cow is infected with the fluke Schistosoma nasale?

a) Constant snoring
b) Wobbly legs
c) Severe flatulence
d) Blindness

12 Why do parrotfish produce a mucus "sleeping bag" for themselves each night?

a) Keep their scent in
b) Stop grit falling on them
c) Protection from predators
d) For warmth

13 Which migratory crab is found on Christmas Island?

a) spotted reef crab
b) Edible crab
c) Fiddler crab
d) Red crab

14 Why is the green basilisk lizard sometimes called the Jesus Christ lizard?

a) It hatches at Christmas
b) It has a healing touch
c) It is found in Jerusalem
d) It can run on water

15 Where might you find the rare red wolf?

a) Australia
b) In a fairy story
c) Ethiopia
d) N America

16 Which animals use heat sensors to find their prey?

a) Moles
b) Some snakes
c) Duck-billed platypus
d) Owls

17 Why do vampire bats produce the protein draculin In their saliva?

a) It stops blood clotting
b) It paralyses victims
c) It anaesthetizes gums
d) It neutralizes pain

18 What are the nests of army ants called?

a) Mounds
b) Hills
c) Galls
d) Bivouacs

19 Which fossil group are birds thought to be the descendants of?

a) Pterosaurs
b) Therapod dinosaurs
c) Stegosaurs
d) Ichthyosaurs

20 To which order do butterflies belong?

a) Hymenoptera
b) Odonata
c) Lepidoptera
d) Diptera

Some **ticks** can **last** for

1 How many chambers does a cow's stomach have?

a 1
b 2
c 3
d 4

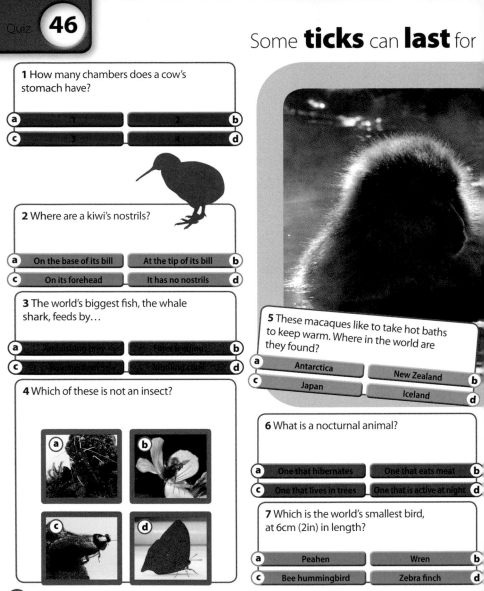

2 Where are a kiwi's nostrils?

a On the base of its bill
b At the tip of its bill
c On its forehead
d It has no nostrils

3 The world's biggest fish, the whale shark, feeds by…

a Ambushing prey
b Filter feeding
c Scavenging
d Nibbling coral

4 Which of these is not an insect?

a
b
c
d

5 These macaques like to take hot baths to keep warm. Where in the world are they found?

a Antarctica
b New Zealand
c Japan
d Iceland

6 What is a nocturnal animal?

a One that hibernates
b One that eats meat
c One that lives in trees
d One that is active at night

7 Which is the world's smallest bird, at 6cm (2in) in length?

a Peahen
b Wren
c Bee hummingbird
d Zebra finch

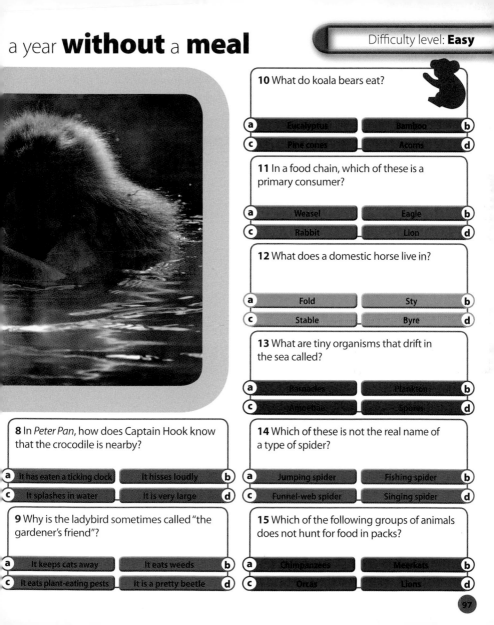

10 What do koala bears eat?

(a) Eucalyptus   (b) Bamboo

(c) Pine cones   (d) Acorns

11 In a food chain, which of these is a primary consumer?

(a) Weasel   (b) Eagle

(c) Rabbit   (d) Lion

12 What does a domestic horse live in?

(a) Fold   (b) Sty

(c) Stable   (d) Byre

13 What are tiny organisms that drift in the sea called?

(a) Barnacles   (b) Plankton

(c) Amoebae   (d) Spores

8 In *Peter Pan*, how does Captain Hook know that the crocodile is nearby?

(a) It has eaten a ticking clock   (b) It hisses loudly

(c) It splashes in water   (d) It is very large

9 Why is the ladybird sometimes called "the gardener's friend"?

(a) It keeps cats away   (b) It eats weeds

(c) It eats plant-eating pests   (d) It is a pretty beetle

14 Which of these is not the real name of a type of spider?

(a) Jumping spider   (b) Fishing spider

(c) Funnel-web spider   (d) Singing spider

15 Which of the following groups of animals does not hunt for food in packs?

(a) Chimpanzees   (b) Meerkats

(c) Orcas   (d) Lions

The **belly** of a **glass frog** is

1 Which animal can hear the lowest frequency of sound?

a Sea lion
b Rhinoceros
c Crocodile
d Elephant

2 Which fierce little mammal is the smallest species of carnivore?

a Little ermine
b Black-footed ferret
c Pine marten
d Least weasel

3 In China, traditional freshwater fishermen use what to catch fish?

a Cormorants
b Spears
c Traps
d Nets

4 Which bird of prey is nicknamed "windhover", because of its hunting technique?

a Goshawk
b Red kite
c Common kestrel
d California condor

5 Which of the following is not another name for scampi?

a Crab
b Langoustine
c Norwegian lobster
d Dublin Bay prawn

6 The word rodent comes from the Latin verb *rodere*, describing which action that rodents do well?

a Gnawing
b Hiding
c Breeding
d Burrowing

7 The world's biggest spider grows up to 28cm (11in) across. What is it called?

a Colossus tarantula
b Blue whale tarantula
c Dragon tarantula
d Goliath tarantula

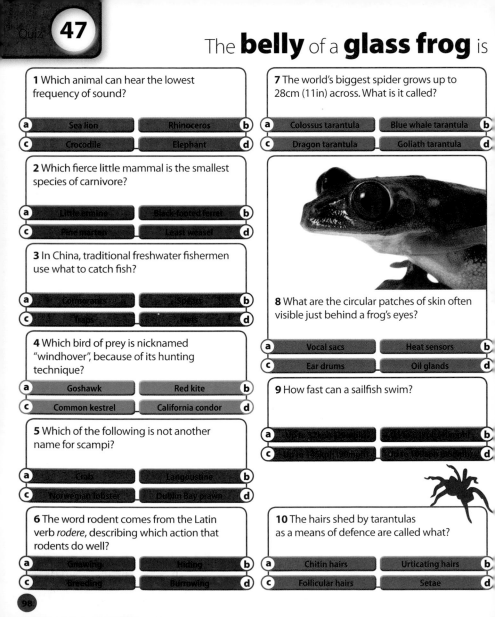

8 What are the circular patches of skin often visible just behind a frog's eyes?

a Vocal sacs
b Heat sensors
c Ear drums
d Oil glands

9 How fast can a sailfish swim?

a Up to 2kph (1.2mph)
b Up to 20kph (12mph)
c Up to 110kph (68mph)
d Up to 190kph (118mph)

10 The hairs shed by tarantulas as a means of defence are called what?

a Chitin hairs
b Urticating hairs
c Follicular hairs
d Setae

transparent, like glass

11 Which is the largest hornbill?

a Wrinkled hornbill
b Southern ground hornbill
c Rhinoceros hornbill
d Great hornbill

12 Which of the cephalopods is considered to be a living fossil?

a Giant Australian cuttlefish
b Nautilus
c Giant octopus
d Vampire squid

13 Where do salmon breed?

a The Sargasso Sea
b Where they hatched
c In shallow coastal waters
d Nobody knows

14 Which breed of horse is used by the Spanish Riding School in Vienna?

a Albino
b Austrian Warmblood
c Lipizzaner
d Thoroughbred

15 What is an aquatic environment with no available oxygen called?

a Low oxygen
b Toxic
c Anaerobic
d Aerobic

16 Why do tortoises sunbathe?

a To drive away lice
b They can't find shade
c To control body heat
d To darken their colour

17 The European mole lives underground. Which of the following does it not have?

a Large eyes
b Shovel-shaped feet
c Side-opening nostrils
d External ears

18 Which snake sprays venom directly into the eyes of its enemies?

a Boa constrictor
b Spitting cobra
c Spitting viper
d Puff adder

19 Which insects squirt formic acid in self defence?

a Wasps
b Weevils
c Ants
d Assassin bugs

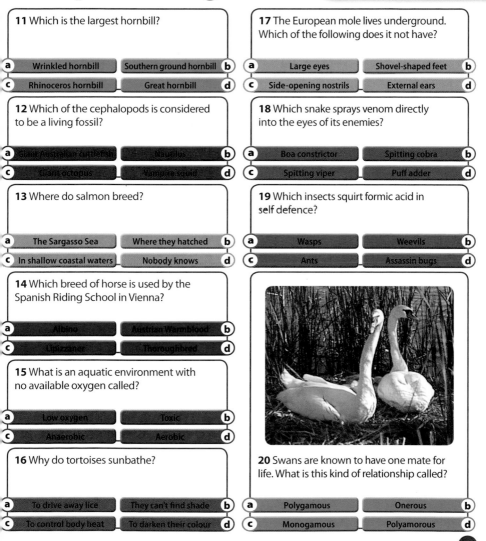

20 Swans are known to have one mate for life. What is this kind of relationship called?

a Polygamous
b Onerous
c Monogamous
d Polyamorous

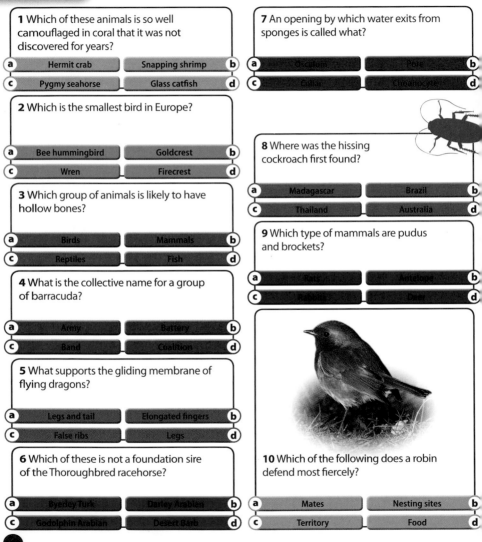

1 Which of these animals is so well camouflaged in coral that it was not discovered for years?

a Hermit crab | b Snapping shrimp
c Pygmy seahorse | d Glass catfish

2 Which is the smallest bird in Europe?

a Bee hummingbird | b Goldcrest
c Wren | d Firecrest

3 Which group of animals is likely to have hollow bones?

a Birds | b Mammals
c Reptiles | d Fish

4 What is the collective name for a group of barracuda?

a Army | b Battery
c Band | d Coalition

5 What supports the gliding membrane of flying dragons?

a Legs and tail | b Elongated fingers
c False ribs | d Legs

6 Which of these is not a foundation sire of the Thoroughbred racehorse?

a Byerley Turk | b Darley Arabian
c Godolphin Arabian | d Desert Barb

7 An opening by which water exits from sponges is called what?

a Osculum | b Pore
c Collar | d Choanocyte

8 Where was the hissing cockroach first found?

a Madagascar | b Brazil
c Thailand | d Australia

9 Which type of mammals are pudus and brockets?

a Rats | b Antelope
c Rabbits | d Deer

10 Which of the following does a robin defend most fiercely?

a Mates | b Nesting sites
c Territory | d Food

distinctive regional **dialects**

11 How do red kangaroos stay cool in hot temperatures?

a) They take shelter
b) They lick their arms
c) They pant
d) They rest in pools

12 Which breed of domestic cattle is famous for its creamy milk?

a) Aberdeen Angus
b) Jersey
c) Brahman
d) Hereford

13 In India, what has driven vultures to the verge of extinction?

a) Loss of habitat
b) Contaminated carcasses
c) Disease
d) Hunting

14 What are the three simple eyes of a dragonfly used for?

a) Orientation
b) Sensing light levels
c) Magnifying objects
d) For 360° vision

15 Which family of fish do humans eat most of?

a) Anchovy
b) Herring
c) Cod
d) Salmon

16 Which echinoderms belong to the class Crinoidea?

a) Sea urchins
b) Starfish
c) Feather stars
d) Sea cucumbers

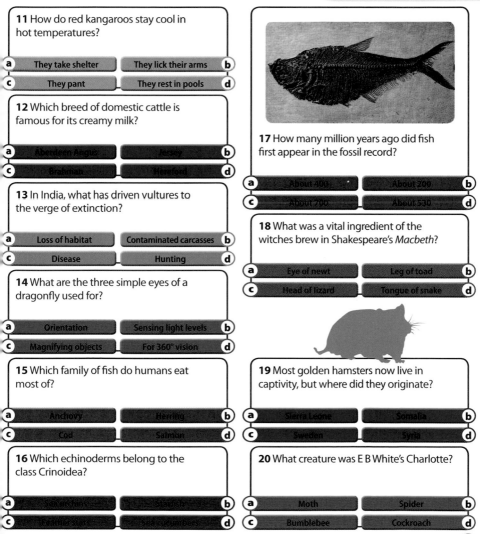

17 How many million years ago did fish first appear in the fossil record?

a) About 400
b) About 200
c) About 700
d) About 530

18 What was a vital ingredient of the witches brew in Shakespeare's *Macbeth*?

a) Eye of newt
b) Leg of toad
c) Head of lizard
d) Tongue of snake

19 Most golden hamsters now live in captivity, but where did they originate?

a) Sierra Leone
b) Somalia
c) Sweden
d) Syria

20 What creature was E B White's Charlotte?

a) Moth
b) Spider
c) Bumblebee
d) Cockroach

Bats' calls are too **high-pitched**

1 What is the correct name for the chisel-like front teeth of rodents and other mammals?

- a) Carnassials
- b) Incisors
- c) Canines
- d) Molars

2 Which of these animals has learned how to open a jar of food?

- a) Octopus
- b) Cat
- c) Rattlesnake
- d) Seal

3 Which of these birds cannot hover?

- a) Herring gull
- b) Hummingbird
- c) Kestrel
- d) Kingfisher

4 Which breed of cattle is traditionally associated with cowboys and the Wild West?

- a) Texas Longhorn
- b) Hereford
- c) Pineywoods
- d) Randall Lineback

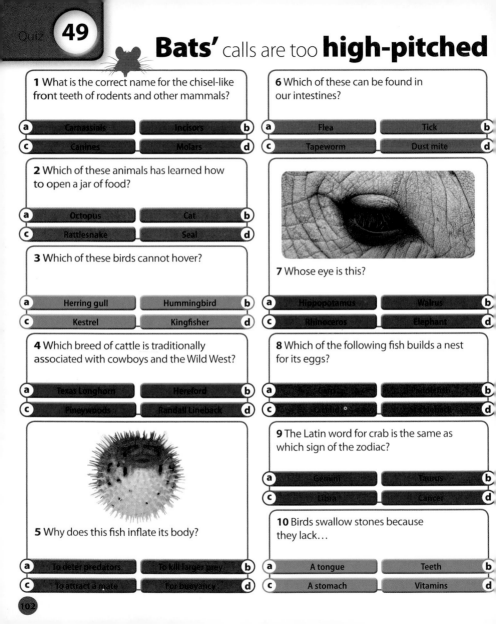

5 Why does this fish inflate its body?

- a) To deter predators
- b) To kill larger prey
- c) To attract a mate
- d) For buoyancy

6 Which of these can be found in our intestines?

- a) Flea
- b) Tick
- c) Tapeworm
- d) Dust mite

7 Whose eye is this?

- a) Hippopotamus
- b) Walrus
- c) Rhinoceros
- d) Elephant

8 Which of the following fish builds a nest for its eggs?

- a) Carp
- b) Dogfish
- c) Catfish
- d) Stickleback

9 The Latin word for crab is the same as which sign of the zodiac?

- a) Gemini
- b) Taurus
- c) Libra
- d) Cancer

10 Birds swallow stones because they lack…

- a) A tongue
- b) Teeth
- c) A stomach
- d) Vitamins

11 Which of the following mammals lays eggs?

a Kangaroo
b Wallaby
c Bat
d Duck-billed platypus

12 What habitat do anacondas live in?

a Grasslands
b Deserts
c Swamps
d Forests

13 Who played Peter Parker in the *Spiderman* films?

a Sam Raimi
b Tobey Maguire
c Willem Dafoe
d James Franco

14 Which gamebird attracts females by displaying its beautiful long tail?

a Quail
b Pheasant
c Willow grouse
d Peacock

15 What does a frog use to help push its food down its throat?

a Its front legs
b Its back legs
c Its eyes
d Its tongue

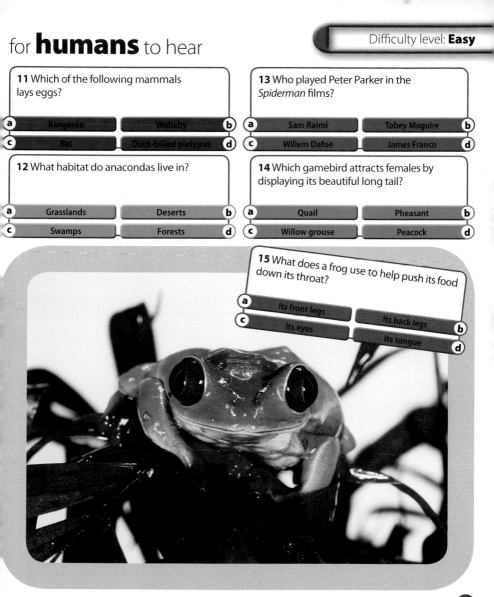

1 Which animal can survive being frozen?

(a) King penguin
(b) Blue-ringed octopus
(c) Yellow seahorse
(d) Wood frog

2 What purpose is served by the long "tail" of a water scorpion bug?

(a) It is a breathing tube
(b) It's used for laying eggs
(c) It is a sting
(d) It's used to impress mates

3 Which reptile from New Zealand is considered to be a living fossil?

(a) Tuatara
(b) Auckland green gecko
(c) Southern skink
(d) Black-eyed gecko

4 The tiny but deadly box jellyfish contains enough venom to kill how many people?

(a) 40
(b) 10
(c) 60
(d) 20

5 Beetles, crabs, spiders, and centipedes are all arthropods. What does the Greek *arthro-poda* mean?

(a) Crunchy body
(b) Creaky legs
(c) Armoured skin
(d) Jointed feet

6 Why is the bumblebee fish so called?

(a) It is striped like a bee
(b) It buzzes like a bee
(c) It stings like a bee
(d) It flies like a bee

7 What alternative name is sometimes used for the European bison?

(a) Wisent
(b) Auroch
(c) American bison
(d) Elk

8 Which mountain range would you be in if you spotted a wild red panda?

(a) Pyrenees
(b) Himalayas
(c) Andes
(d) Urals

9 Which is the most dangerous of the cephalopods?

(a) Glass squid
(b) Blue-ringed octopus
(c) Dumbo octopus
(d) Common squid

10 Male anglerfish have what type of relationship with females?

(a) Mutualistic
(b) Commensal
(c) No relationship
(d) Parasitic

11 Many grassland habitats depend on which beetles to maintain soil quality?

a Longhorn beetles
b Stag beetles
c Dung beetles
d Leaf beetles

12 A woodpecker has four toes. How many of them point forwards?

a 2
b 3
c 4
d 1

13 In order to prevent damage to their ears, bats…

a Lay them flat
b Put their wings over them
c Turn their ears away
d Close a flap inside the ear

14 Which comic did the superhero Spiderman appear in?

a Eagle
b Marvel Comics
c The Beano
d DC Comics

15 Which is the deepest diving mammal, thought to be able to reach depths of 3km (2 miles)?

a Blue whale
b California sea lion
c Emperor penguin
d Sperm whale

16 After making a kill, where might a leopard store the carcass?

a Underground
b Under rocks
c They don't stash food
d In the branches of a tree

17 Where are cassowaries found?

a Eurasia
b Antarctica
c New Guinea; Australia
d The Americas

18 When fully stretched, spider silk is as strong as the same thickness of which man-made material?

a PVC
b Polystyrene
c Steel
d Nylon

19 What are the different sections of a tortoise's shell called?

a Scales
b Scutes
c Osteophytes
d Panels

20 Which birds are well known for their dazzling courtship displays?

a Birds of prey
b Seabirds
c Gamebirds
d Birds of paradise

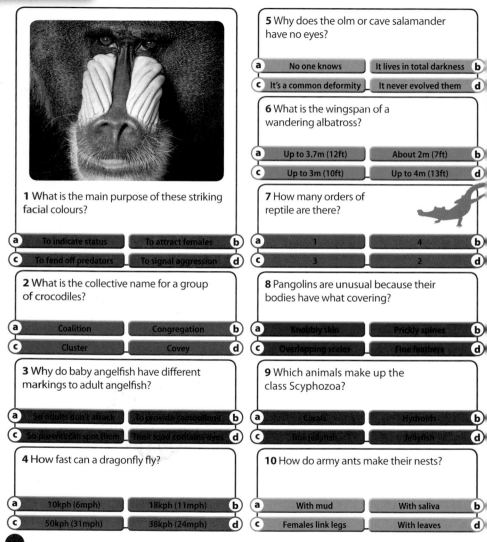

1 What is the main purpose of these striking facial colours?

a To indicate status
b To attract females
c To fend off predators
d To signal aggression

2 What is the collective name for a group of crocodiles?

a Coalition
b Congregation
c Cluster
d Covey

3 Why do baby angelfish have different markings to adult angelfish?

a So adults don't attack
b To provide camouflage
c So parents can spot them
d Their food contains dyes

4 How fast can a dragonfly fly?

a 10kph (6mph)
b 18kph (11mph)
c 50kph (31mph)
d 38kph (24mph)

5 Why does the olm or cave salamander have no eyes?

a No one knows
b It lives in total darkness
c It's a common deformity
d It never evolved them

6 What is the wingspan of a wandering albatross?

a Up to 3.7m (12ft)
b About 2m (7ft)
c Up to 3m (10ft)
d Up to 4m (13ft)

7 How many orders of reptile are there?

a 1
b 4
c 3
d 2

8 Pangolins are unusual because their bodies have what covering?

a Knobbly skin
b Prickly spines
c Overlapping scales
d Fine feathers

9 Which animals make up the class Scyphozoa?

a Corals
b Hydroids
c Box jellyfish
d Jellyfish

10 How do army ants make their nests?

a With mud
b With saliva
c Females link legs
d With leaves

11 To which phylum do sponges belong?

a Platyhelminthes   b Porifera

c Annelida   d Echinodermata

12 Which of the following adaptations is not usually an adaptation for predation?

a Strong jaw   b Forward-facing eyes

c Wide cheekbones   d Long tongue

13 Which Egyptian god Is depicted with the head of an ibis?

a Thoth   b Ra

c Anubis   d Hathor

14 What is the collective name for a group of salmon?

a Pod   b Bunch

c Colony   d Cluster

15 How many eyes does a dragonfly have?

a 3   b 5

c 4   d 2

16 Which of the following are most closely related?

a Seal and sea lion   b Whale and dolphin

c Wild ass and zebra   d Bear and tiger

17 In the late 19th century, which industry led to huge demand for great egret feathers?

a Hat-making (millinery)   b Tailoring

c Shoe-making   d Mattress-making

18 Which is the only jawless fish alive today?

a Lamprey   b Angelfish

c Eel   d Turbot

19 Which type of mammal has the largest eyes relative to its body size?

a Whale   b Frog

c Tarsier   d Cat

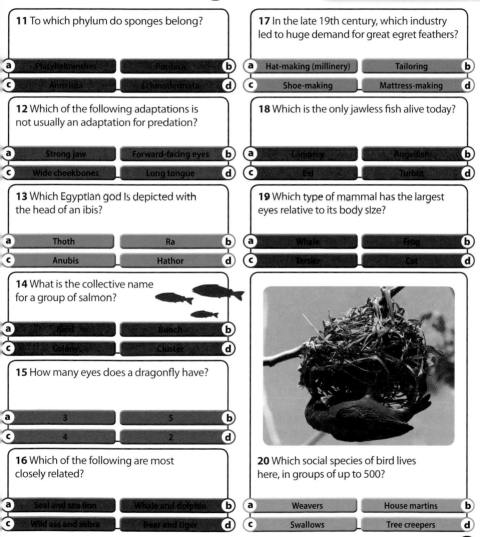

20 Which social species of bird lives here, in groups of up to 500?

a Weavers   b House martins

c Swallows   d Tree creepers

Snakes can't **chew**, so they

1 What are prairie dog colonies called?

a Cities
b Hamlets
c Villages
d Towns

2 Which of these is not a feature common to all mammals?

a Mostly have hair
b Warm-blooded
c Four legs
d Mammary glands

3 What do most crustaceans have on the outside of their bodies?

a Endoskeleton
b Tentacles
c Shells
d Exoskeleton

4 How many body segments does a spider have?

a 4
b 5
c 2
d 3

5 Hummingbirds feed on…

a Fruit
b Pollen
c Flying insects
d Nectar

swallow their prey **whole**

6 What colour is an adult emerald tree boa?

a Blue

b Green

c Red

d Yellow

7 370,000 – it's a big number. What is 370,000 the number of?

a Known beetle species

b Animals on Earth

c Dinosaur fossils found

d Extinct animal species

8 What type of animal am I?

a Gecko

b Iguana

c Skink

d Chameleon

9 Which of these is the smelliest mammal?

a Skunk

b Raccoon

c Weasel

d Musk ox

10 Where do polar bears spend most of their time?

a On refuse tips

b On sea ice

c In the sea

d In rivers

11 What word is used to describe a group of chicks in a nest?

a Litter

b Brood

c Clutch

d Brethren

12 Which breed of dog is the most popular worldwide?

a Border Terrier

b Labrador Retriever

c Cocker Spaniel

d Poodle

13 I am a very well-camouflaged invertebrate. What am I?

a Sea snake

b Stick insect

c Hermit crab

d King prawn

14 Which zodiac sign takes its name from fish?

a Pisces

b Virgo

c Sagittarios

d Libra

15 I am the world's largest bird. What am I?

a Ostrich

b Emu

c King penguin

d Flamingo

Sperm whales are the

1 Which animal cannot move its eyes independently of each other?

(a) Seahorse
(b) Mantis shrimp
(c) Chameleon
(d) Sheep

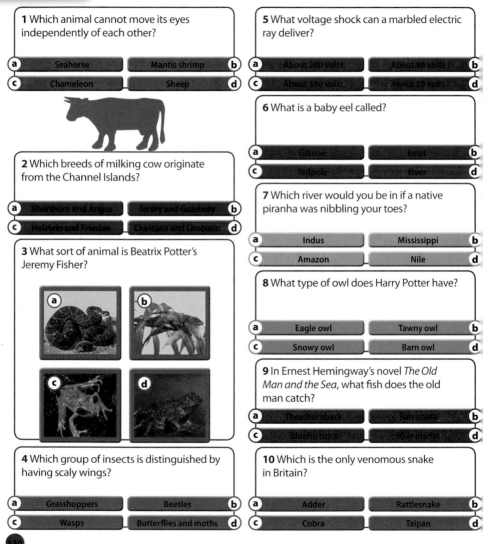

2 Which breeds of milking cow originate from the Channel Islands?

(a) Shorthorn and Angus
(b) Jersey and Guernsey
(c) Holstein and Friesian
(d) Charolais and Limousin

3 What sort of animal is Beatrix Potter's Jeremy Fisher?

(a)
(b)
(c)
(d)

4 Which group of insects is distinguished by having scaly wings?

(a) Grasshoppers
(b) Beetles
(c) Wasps
(d) Butterflies and moths

5 What voltage shock can a marbled electric ray deliver?

(a) About 200 volts
(b) About 80 volts
(c) About 350 volts
(d) About 20 volts

6 What is a baby eel called?

(a) Glassie
(b) Eelet
(c) Tadpole
(d) Elver

7 Which river would you be in if a native piranha was nibbling your toes?

(a) Indus
(b) Mississippi
(c) Amazon
(d) Nile

8 What type of owl does Harry Potter have?

(a) Eagle owl
(b) Tawny owl
(c) Snowy owl
(d) Barn owl

9 In Ernest Hemingway's novel *The Old Man and the Sea*, what fish does the old man catch?

(a) Thresher shark
(b) Barracuda
(c) Bluefin tuna
(d) Blue marlin

10 Which is the only venomous snake in Britain?

(a) Adder
(b) Rattlesnake
(c) Cobra
(d) Taipan

loudest animals on **Earth**

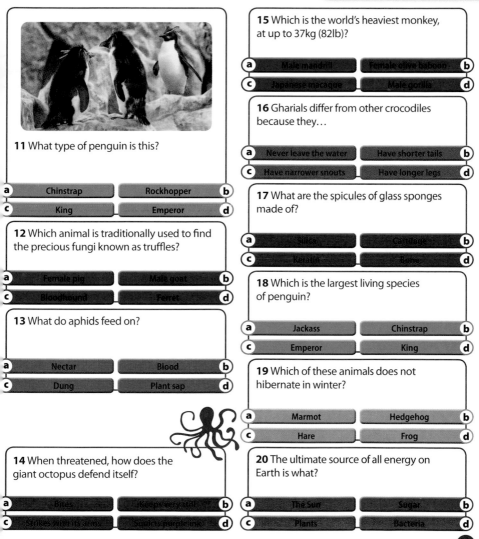

11 What type of penguin is this?

| a | Chinstrap | Rockhopper | b |
| c | King | Emperor | d |

12 Which animal is traditionally used to find the precious fungi known as truffles?

| a | Female pig | Male goat | b |
| c | Bloodhound | Ferret | d |

13 What do aphids feed on?

| a | Nectar | Blood | b |
| c | Dung | Plant sap | d |

14 When threatened, how does the giant octopus defend itself?

| a | Bites | Keeps very still | b |
| c | Strikes with its arms | Squirts purple ink | d |

15 Which is the world's heaviest monkey, at up to 37kg (82lb)?

| a | Male mandrill | Female olive baboon | b |
| c | Japanese macaque | Male gorilla | d |

16 Gharials differ from other crocodiles because they…

| a | Never leave the water | Have shorter tails | b |
| c | Have narrower snouts | Have longer legs | d |

17 What are the spicules of glass sponges made of?

| a | Silica | Cartilage | b |
| c | Keratin | Bone | d |

18 Which is the largest living species of penguin?

| a | Jackass | Chinstrap | b |
| c | Emperor | King | d |

19 Which of these animals does not hibernate in winter?

| a | Marmot | Hedgehog | b |
| c | Hare | Frog | d |

20 The ultimate source of all energy on Earth is what?

| a | The Sun | Sugar | b |
| c | Plants | Bacteria | d |

Termite populations outweigh

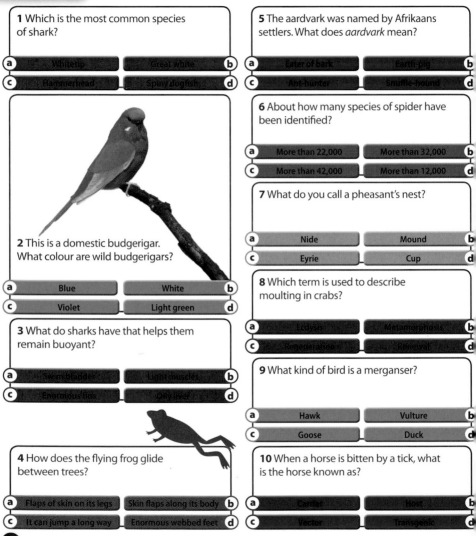

1 Which is the most common species of shark?

- **a** Whitetip
- **b** Great white
- **c** Hammerhead
- **d** Spiny dogfish

2 This is a domestic budgerigar. What colour are wild budgerigars?

- **a** Blue
- **b** White
- **c** Violet
- **d** Light green

3 What do sharks have that helps them remain buoyant?

- **a** Swim bladder
- **b** Light muscles
- **c** Enormous fins
- **d** Oily liver

4 How does the flying frog glide between trees?

- **a** Flaps of skin on its legs
- **b** Skin flaps along its body
- **c** It can jump a long way
- **d** Enormous webbed feet

5 The aardvark was named by Afrikaans settlers. What does *aardvark* mean?

- **a** Eater of bark
- **b** Earth-pig
- **c** Ant-hunter
- **d** Snuffle-hound

6 About how many species of spider have been identified?

- **a** More than 22,000
- **b** More than 32,000
- **c** More than 42,000
- **d** More than 12,000

7 What do you call a pheasant's nest?

- **a** Nide
- **b** Mound
- **c** Eyrie
- **d** Cup

8 Which term is used to describe moulting in crabs?

- **a** Ecdysis
- **b** Metamorphosis
- **c** Regeneration
- **d** Renewal

9 What kind of bird is a merganser?

- **a** Hawk
- **b** Vulture
- **c** Goose
- **d** Duck

10 When a horse is bitten by a tick, what is the horse known as?

- **a** Carrier
- **b** Host
- **c** Vector
- **d** Transgenic

11 What is the collective name for a group of flying fish?

a Shoal
b Family
c Cluster
d Glide

12 Which unique feature defines cnidarians, which include jellyfish and corals?

a
b
c
d

13 What is the collective name for a group of caterpillars?

a Drove
b Army
c Band
d Troop

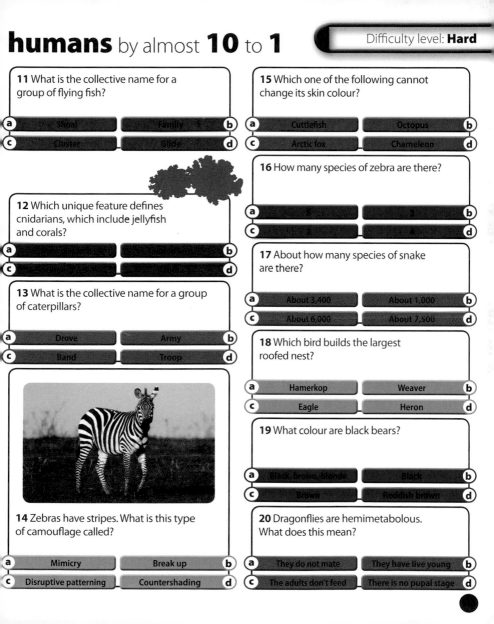

14 Zebras have stripes. What is this type of camouflage called?

a Mimicry
b Break up
c Disruptive patterning
d Countershading

15 Which one of the following cannot change its skin colour?

a Cuttlefish
b Octopus
c Arctic fox
d Chameleon

16 How many species of zebra are there?

a
b
c 2
d 4

17 About how many species of snake are there?

a About 3,400
b About 1,000
c About 6,000
d About 7,500

18 Which bird builds the largest roofed nest?

a Hamerkop
b Weaver
c Eagle
d Heron

19 What colour are black bears?

a Black, brown, blonde
b Black
c Brown
d Reddish brown

20 Dragonflies are hemimetabolous. What does this mean?

a They do not mate
b They have live young
c The adults don't feed
d There is no pupal stage

A **newborn kangaroo** is

1 I am an amphibian with a tail. What am I?

- **a** Snake
- **b** Lizard
- **c** Toad
- **d** Newt

2 Which of these is not a group of mammals?

- **a** Primates
- **b** Rodents
- **c** Tortoises
- **d** Bats

3 I am a baby insect. What do I grow into?

- **a** Ladybird
- **b** Wasp
- **c** Dragonfly
- **d** Bumblebee

4 Which is the only seal to live in fresh water?

- **a** Caspian
- **b** Baikal
- **c** Ross
- **d** Harp

5 Where do Atlantic puffins lay their eggs?

- **a** On shingle beaches
- **b** On sandy beaches
- **c** In clifftop burrows
- **d** On cliff ledges

6 All of these insects live in colonies except one – which is it?

- **a** Leafcutter ant
- **b** Harvester termite
- **c** House fly
- **d** Honeybee

7 Which animal bends its "knees" backwards?

- **a** Shrew
- **b** Badger
- **c** Flamingo
- **d** Hippopotamus

the **size** of a **peanut**

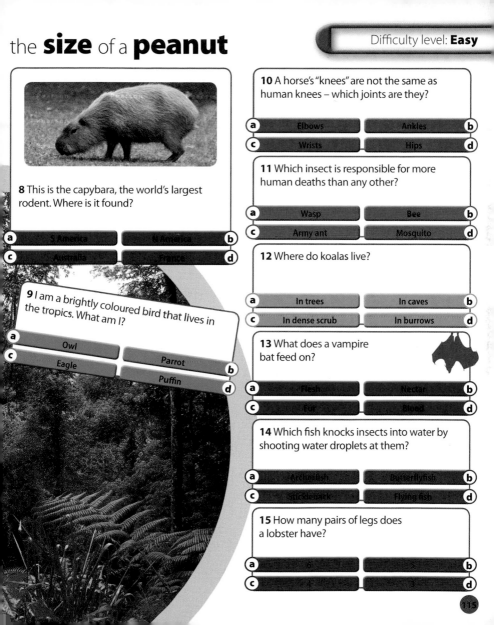

8 This is the capybara, the world's largest rodent. Where is it found?

a. S America
b. N America
c. Australia
d. France

9 I am a brightly coloured bird that lives in the tropics. What am I?

a. Owl
b. Parrot
c. Eagle
d. Puffin

10 A horse's "knees" are not the same as human knees – which joints are they?

a. Elbows
b. Ankles
c. Wrists
d. Hips

11 Which insect is responsible for more human deaths than any other?

a. Wasp
b. Bee
c. Army ant
d. Mosquito

12 Where do koalas live?

a. In trees
b. In caves
c. In dense scrub
d. In burrows

13 What does a vampire bat feed on?

a. Flesh
b. Nectar
c. Fur
d. Blood

14 Which fish knocks insects into water by shooting water droplets at them?

a. Archerfish
b. Butterflyfish
c. Stickleback
d. Flying fish

15 How many pairs of legs does a lobster have?

a. 6
b. 5
c. 4
d. 3

115

Chameleons can **look** in **opposite**

1 In which book did Darwin suggest that humans and apes share a common ancestor?

(a) *The Descent of Man*
(b) *On the Origin of Species*
(c) *The Voyage of the Beagle*
(d) *He didn't suggest this*

2 How big is a newborn red kangaroo?

(a) Size of a kitten
(b) Half its mother's size
(c) Size of a peanut
(d) Size of a plum

3 Which member of the snail family can inject a deadly neurotoxin when picked up?

(a) Whelk
(b) Unicorn shell
(c) Cone shell
(d) Trumpet snail

4 Where would you go to see a springhare?

(a) Europe
(b) Asia
(c) Africa
(d) America

5 What is the sweet, sticky liquid secreted by aphids called?

(a) Nectar
(b) Sweetener
(c) Honeydew
(d) Sugar

6 When did reptiles first appear in the fossil record?

(a) Permian
(b) Carboniferous
(c) Triassic
(d) Jurassic

7 Which small crustaceans are the favourite food of the blue whale?

(a) Plankton
(b) Krill
(c) Copepods
(d) Whale lice

8 Tapeworms live in the gut of larger animals and steal their food. How long can a tapeworm grow?

(a) Up to 50cm (20in)
(b) Over 15m (49ft)
(c) Up to 5m (16ft)
(d) Up to 10m (33ft)

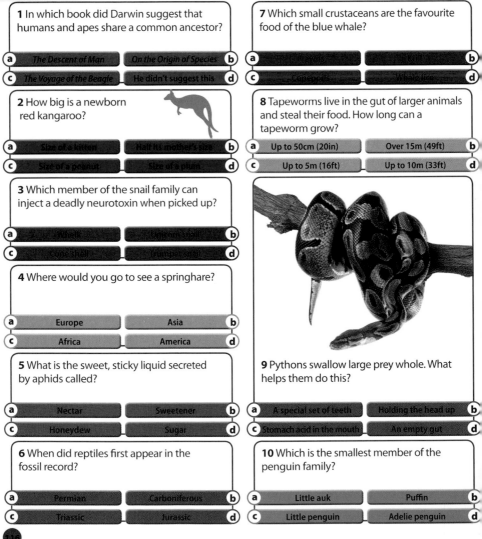

9 Pythons swallow large prey whole. What helps them do this?

(a) A special set of teeth
(b) Holding the head up
(c) Stomach acid in the mouth
(d) An empty gut

10 Which is the smallest member of the penguin family?

(a) Little auk
(b) Puffin
(c) Little penguin
(d) Adelie penguin

directions at the **same** time

11 Which of the following is a significant threat to the survival of seahorses?

- **a** Global warming
- **b** Scuba divers
- **c** Chinese medicine
- **d** Overfishing

12 What is the cuttle of a cuttlefish?

- **a**
- **b**
- **c**
- **d**

13 Flies soften their food by spitting on it. They then ingest it with mouthparts that work like a…

- **a** Pair of scissors
- **b** Sponge
- **c** Hypodermic syringe
- **d** Ladle

14 What are American marmots also known as?

- **a** Mountain beavers
- **b** Chipmunks
- **c** Rock bunnies
- **d** Woodchucks

15 Which is the largest of the US songbirds?

- **a** American robin
- **b** Common raven
- **c** Eastern meadowlark
- **d** Bullock's oriole

16 Which group of animals cannot echolocate?

- **a** Shrews
- **b** Bats
- **c** Turtles
- **d** Dolphins

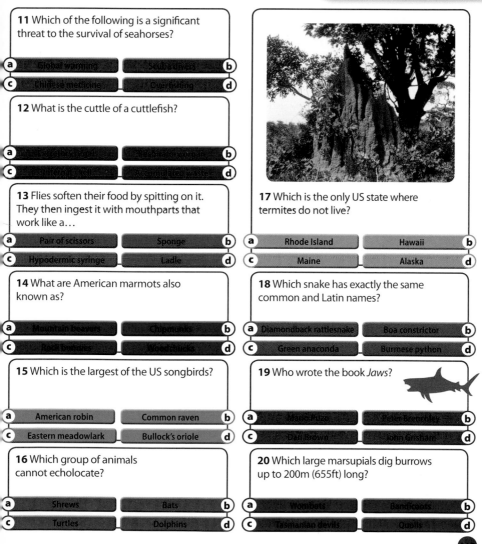

17 Which is the only US state where termites do not live?

- **a** Rhode Island
- **b** Hawaii
- **c** Maine
- **d** Alaska

18 Which snake has exactly the same common and Latin names?

- **a** Diamondback rattlesnake
- **b** Boa constrictor
- **c** Green anaconda
- **d** Burmese python

19 Who wrote the book *Jaws*?

- **a** Mario Puzo
- **b** Peter Brenchley
- **c** Dan Brown
- **d** John Grisham

20 Which large marsupials dig burrows up to 200m (655ft) long?

- **a** Wombats
- **b** Bandicoots
- **c** Tasmanian devils
- **d** Quolls

Aphids are born **pregnant**, and can

1 The lack of genetic variation in cheetahs has been attributed to what?

a. Genetic bottleneck
b. Competition
c. Isolation
d. Outcrossing

2 What are the algae that live in cells of reef-building corals called?

a. Kelp
b. Zooxanthellae
c. Seaweed
d. Rhodophyta

3 An elephant's trunk is made up of its…

a. Nose and upper lip
b. Nose
c. Upper lip
d. Lower lip

4 Which of the following lacks an anal fin?

a. Angelfish
b. Pike
c. Sawfish
d. Whale shark

5 What kind of bird is the flightless kakapo from New Zealand?

a. Owl
b. Emu
c. Parrot
d. Kiwi

6 About how long do most adult May bugs live for?

a. About a month
b. About a year
c. About a week
d. About a day

7 Which of the following is an early fossil amphibian?

a. Eryops
b. Triadobatrachus
c. Eodiscoglossus
d. Ichthyostega

8 What is the collective name for a group of trout?

a. Aggregation
b. Knot
c. Hover
d. Mob

9 Which bird are chickens thought to be descended from?

a. Great argus
b. Helmeted guineafowl
c. Red junglefowl
d. Mallee fowl

10 How many pairs of eyes do most spiders have?

a. 3
b. 4
c. 1
d. 2

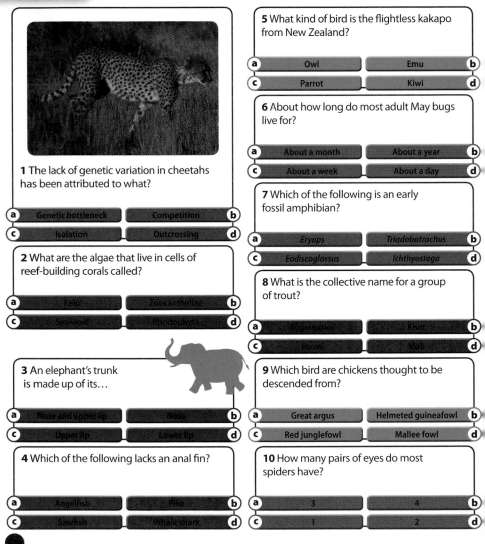

give **birth** when 10 days old

Difficulty level: **Hard**

11 Which land mammal has the densest fur?

a Chinchilla
b Snow leopard
c Arctic fox
d Musk ox

12 To which class of mollusc does the octopus belong?

a Cephalopoda
b Gastropoda
c Bivalvia
d Scaphopoda

13 Fish that can live in fresh, brackish, or saltwater habitats are called what?

a Ectothermic
b Euryhaline
c Marine
d Endothermic

14 Which Egyptian god is depicted with the head of a falcon?

a Osiris
b Seth
c Sobek
d Ra

15 Which is the smallest of the whales?

a Dwarf sperm whale
b Beluga
c Narwhal
d Pilot whale

16 Which of these birds lives in an adherent nest, which is usually built against a wall?

a Starling
b Robin
c Kingfisher
d Swift

17 Which is the largest shark that ever lived?

a Squalus
b Isurus
c Megalodon
d Carcharodon

18 What is the collective name for a group of rattlesnakes?

a Rhumba
b Seething
c Rattle
d Tower

19 How much energy is passed from one level of a food chain to the next?

a About 80 per cent
b About 10 per cent
c About 40 per cent
d About 65 per cent

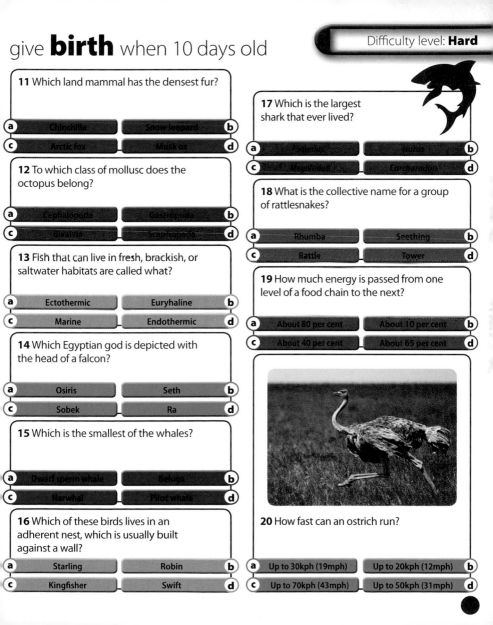

20 How fast can an ostrich run?

a Up to 30kph (19mph)
b Up to 20kph (12mph)
c Up to 70kph (43mph)
d Up to 50kph (31mph)

A **blue-ringed** octopus has enough

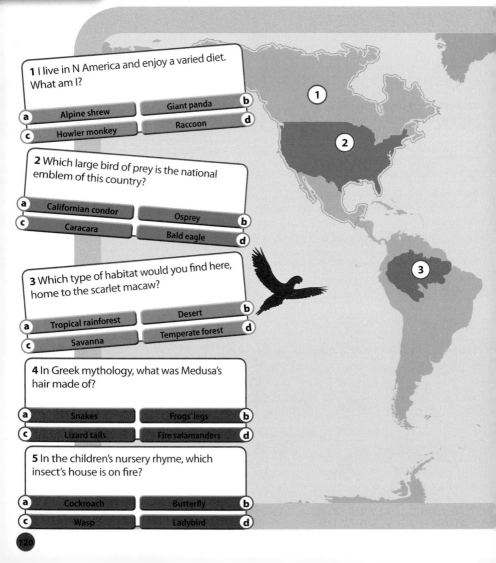

1 I live in N America and enjoy a varied diet. What am I?

- a Alpine shrew
- b Giant panda
- c Howler monkey
- d Raccoon

2 Which large bird of prey is the national emblem of this country?

- a Californian condor
- b Osprey
- c Caracara
- d Bald eagle

3 Which type of habitat would you find here, home to the scarlet macaw?

- a Tropical rainforest
- b Desert
- c Savanna
- d Temperate forest

4 In Greek mythology, what was Medusa's hair made of?

- a Snakes
- b Frogs' legs
- c Lizard tails
- d Fire salamanders

5 In the children's nursery rhyme, which insect's house is on fire?

- a Cockroach
- b Butterfly
- c Wasp
- d Ladybird

6 Which is the smallest breed of dog?

a Chihuahua
b Mexican Hairless
c Papillon
d Toy Fox Terrier

7 The leafy seadragon is camouflaged to look like what?

a Another fish
b The sea bed
c Seaweed
d Coral

8 Which molluscs produce the pearls used in jewellery?

a Sea slug
b Oysters
c Clams
d Limpets

9 In a food chain, which of these is a producer?

a Zebra
b Leafcutter ant
c Grass
d Rabbit

10 Which insect carries malaria?

a Mosquito
b Tick
c Gnat
d Bed bug

11 What important job do bacteria do in the stomach of a cow?

a Kill other organisms
b Produce stomach acid
c Help break down food
d None of these

12 Which one of the following moves using water-filled tube feet?

a Maggot
b Slow worm
c Frog
d Sea urchin

13 What animal is this?

a Walrus
b Rhinoceros
c Elephant
d Hippopotamus

14 Where do giant tortoises come from?

a Mauritius
b Crete
c Sri Lanka
d Galapagos Islands

15 Ratite birds cannot do what?

a Run fast
b Peck
c Fly
d Lay eggs

Male **Dayak fruit bats** are the **only**

1 Which order of birds contains the most species?

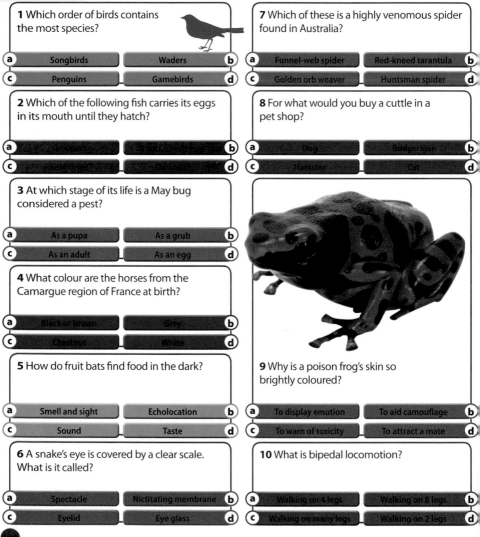

a. Songbirds
b. Waders
c. Penguins
d. Gamebirds

2 Which of the following fish carries its eggs in its mouth until they hatch?

a. Groupers
b. Cichlids
c. Seahorses
d. Damselfish

3 At which stage of its life is a May bug considered a pest?

a. As a pupa
b. As a grub
c. As an adult
d. As an egg

4 What colour are the horses from the Camargue region of France at birth?

a. Black or brown
b. Grey
c. Chestnut
d. White

5 How do fruit bats find food in the dark?

a. Smell and sight
b. Echolocation
c. Sound
d. Taste

6 A snake's eye is covered by a clear scale. What is it called?

a. Spectacle
b. Nictitating membrane
c. Eyelid
d. Eye glass

7 Which of these is a highly venomous spider found in Australia?

a. Funnel-web spider
b. Red-kneed tarantula
c. Golden orb weaver
d. Huntsman spider

8 For what would you buy a cuttle in a pet shop?

a. Dog
b. Budgerigar
c. Hamster
d. Cat

9 Why is a poison frog's skin so brightly coloured?

a. To display emotion
b. To aid camouflage
c. To warn of toxicity
d. To attract a mate

10 What is bipedal locomotion?

a. Walking on 4 legs
b. Walking on 8 legs
c. Walking on many legs
d. Walking on 2 legs

male mammals that **lactate**

11 Herbivores cannot digest plant cellulose. How does it get broken down?

a Worms in the intestines   Stomach acid b

c It breaks down naturally   Bacteria in the stomach d

12 Which of these birds lays its eggs in another species' nest and lets them bring up its young?

a Cuckoo   Robin b

c Magpie   Bearded tit d

13 The depression or flattened grass that forms a hare's nest is called what?

a Form   Hutch b

c Cup   Scrape d

14 Sponges only possess one of these features. Which is it?

a Body symmetry   Organs b

c Nerves   Spicules d

15 Shark teeth fall out often and have to be replaced regularly. How long do most shark teeth last?

a A few months   About a year b

c More than 5 years   About a week d

16 Which rodent was blamed for spreading the deadly bubonic plague?

a Spiny rat   Brown rat b

c Black rat   House mouse d

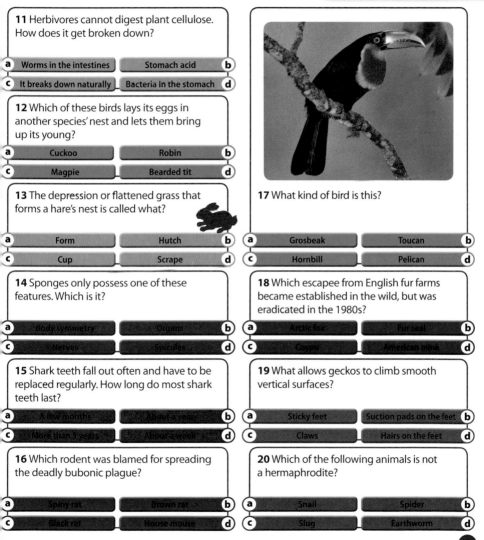

17 What kind of bird is this?

a Grosbeak   Toucan b

c Hornbill   Pelican d

18 Which escapee from English fur farms became established in the wild, but was eradicated in the 1980s?

a Arctic fox   Fur seal b

c Coypu   American mink d

19 What allows geckos to climb smooth vertical surfaces?

a Sticky feet   Suction pads on the feet b

c Claws   Hairs on the feet d

20 Which of the following animals is not a hermaphrodite?

a Snail   Spider b

c Slug   Earthworm d

1 What is the longest leap recorded for a frog?

(a) 3m (10ft)
(b) 7m (23ft)
(c) 5.3m (17ft)
(d) 2m (6ft)

2 The modified inner edges of a male shark's pelvic fins are called…

(a) Pelvic organs
(b) Claspers
(c) Spines
(d) Extensions

3 Which is the most venomous spider in the world?

(a) Brazilian wandering spider
(b) Redback spider
(c) Huntsman spider
(d) Black widow

4 Which eagle eats sloths and monkeys?

(a) Bateleur
(b) Harpy
(c) Martial
(d) Golden

5 In *Jaws*, the population of which island is terrorized by a great white shark?

(a) Long Island
(b) Amity Island
(c) Block Island
(d) Fiji

6 Which is the largest sea slug?

(a) Spanish dancer
(b) Hermissenda
(c) Sea hare
(d) Chromodorid sea slug

7 Which mammal has the longest annual migration?

(a) Black wildebeest
(b) Blue whale
(c) Reindeer
(d) Humpback whale

8 What does this snapping turtle do to attract prey?

(a) Makes a snapping sound
(b) Produces pheromones
(c) Smells of rotten fish
(d) Wiggles its pink tongue

9 Which of the following is true of biomass in a food chain?

(a) Decreases from bottom up
(b) Decreases from top down
(c) It stays the same
(d) Varies according to level

10 How long does it take a koala to eat 500g (1lb) of eucalyptus leaves?

(a) 20 minutes
(b) 12 hours
(c) 6 hours
(d) 4 hours

11 Which type of birds build pendant nests?

a Wrens   b Pigeons

c Weavers   d Swallows

12 How many million years ago did cnidarians first appear in the fossil record?

a About 300   b About 100

c About 500   d About 400

13 Which is the world's slowest mammal?

a Long-nosed echidna   b Manatee

c Orangutan   d Three-toed sloth

14 Fish with dark backs and light bellies are said to be what?

a Countercoloured   b Countershaded

c Two-tone   d Bicoloured

15 Which order of insects do bugs belong to?

a Coleoptera   b Mantodea

c Hemiptera   d Lepidoptera

16 How does a beaver store vegetation to keep it fresh for the winter?

a It forms part of the dam   b In its lodge

c No store is necessary   d In its lake, in cold water

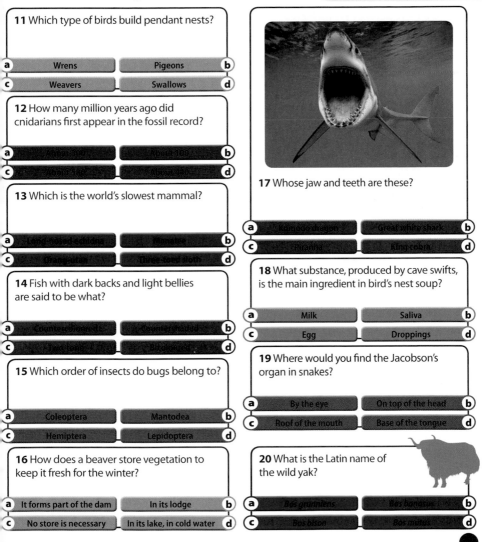

17 Whose jaw and teeth are these?

a Komodo dragon   b Great white shark

c Piranha   d King cobra

18 What substance, produced by cave swifts, is the main ingredient in bird's nest soup?

a Milk   b Saliva

c Egg   d Droppings

19 Where would you find the Jacobson's organ in snakes?

a By the eye   b On top of the head

c Roof of the mouth   d Base of the tongue

20 What is the Latin name of the wild yak?

a Bos grunniens   b Bos bonasus

c Bos bison   d Bos mutus

What is an animal?

More than a million different types of animals have been scientifically described and named – and more are discovered every day. Their variety of form and size is astonishing, ranging from tiny wasps just a tenth of a millimetre (0.004in) long to the colossal 30m (98ft) blue whale. Some are very familiar, while others are barely recognizable as animals. But, despite their diversity, they all share a set of features that distinguish them from other forms of life on Earth.

The animal kingdom

Animals form one of the six "kingdoms" of life, which each function in very different ways. The other kingdoms consist of plants, fungi, microscopic single-celled bacteria and archaea, and the mainly microscopic protists such as algae.

Food and energy

A plant uses the energy of the Sun to make food from simple chemicals. Animals cannot do this, and instead they eat the food made by plants, turning some of it back into energy. Some animals eat other animals, but if a bird eats this caterpillar it is still eating food that was originally made by a plant.

Vital oxygen

Plants turn water and carbon dioxide into food that stores solar energy. This produces oxygen, which animals breathe in to reverse the process and turn some of their food back into energy, carbon dioxide, and water. The waste water that they breathe out is visible on a cold day.

Senses and brains

Even the simplest animals can sense what is going on around them, and react to it. Most have several senses such as sight, touch, and smell. These are linked to a brain that processes and memorizes the information so the animal can use it. The result is behaviour – something unique to animals.

Brain controls
snake's actions

Forked tongue
picks up scents

Getting about

The most obvious feature of an animal is that it moves. Some simple creatures may not move much, but many other animals, like this cheetah, can move very fast indeed. It enables them to catch or find food, escape or hide from enemies, and look for breeding partners.

Amazing diversity

Think of a typical animal, and you probably imagine a mammal or a bird. But animal life is far more diverse than this. Most animals, such as this marine worm, are quite unlike those we think "typical", and the vertebrates – which include mammals and birds – make up just two per cent of known animal species.

Evolution

Life is hard, so any animal that enjoys some advantage over others will be more likely to survive and breed. This is the process of natural selection. It has driven the evolution of all animal species on Earth – and the extinction of countless others like this fossil trilobite.

127

Marine invertebrates

Most of the animals on the planet are invertebrates – creatures that do not have backbones. Many of these live in the oceans. They include animals as diverse as armoured crabs, spiny sea urchins, and soft-bodied jellyfish, and range in size from near-microscopic creatures living in the plankton to giant squid up to 14m (46ft) long. They exist in vast numbers, forming a vital part of the oceanic food chain.

Corals and anemones

Sea anemones such as these cling to rocks and use stinging tentacles to catch prey. Corals are similar, but many contain food-making algae, and have stony skeletons that form rocky reefs.

Jellyfish

Among the simplest of all animals, jellyfish are close relatives of corals and anemones that swim or drift through the oceans. They feed by snaring other animals in tentacles armed with thousands of stinging cells. The venom of some is powerful enough to kill a human.

Crabs and crayfish

Many oceanic animals are crustaceans – creatures with jointed external skeletons. Some are very small, delicate creatures that drift near the surface. Others, like this marine crayfish, crawl on the sea bed.

Blue-ringed
octopus has a
venomous bite

Clams and snails

Typical molluscs have
strong shells to protect
their soft bodies. Some,
like this giant clam, are
bivalves with two
hinged shells. Others
such as snails have one
shell. Bivalves like clams
and mussels generally
stay in one place and
filter the water for food,
but many marine snails
are active predators.

Octopus, cuttlefish, and squid

Most marine invertebrates are quite
simple animals, but octopuses and their
relatives are active hunters with highly
developed senses. They are amazingly
intelligent, considering they are
molluscs, related to clams and snails.

Feathery arms catch
drifting animals

Starfish and sea urchins

Some of the strangest sea creatures are the
echinoderms – starfish, sea urchins, and
their relatives. Their bodies have a radial
plan, like wheels. Some crawl on the sea bed,
but others, like this featherstar, cling to rocks.

Insects and spiders

Insects are the most successful animals on Earth, accounting for 85 per cent of all known animal species. Most are very small, simply because their anatomy makes large size impossible. But they exist in huge numbers – some 200 million for every person on the planet – and are a vital part of the web of life.

Grasshoppers

Long-legged grasshoppers use their powerful jaws to eat tough plants, and some – the locusts – form vast swarms that devastate farm crops. Unlike most insects, they hatch from the egg as baby versions of the adults, and grow bigger by stages.

Dragonflies

Fast, agile dragonflies use their amazing flying skills to seize other insects in mid-air, targeting them with huge eyes that have up to 30,000 tiny lenses each. All adult insects have similar compound eyes, which are very sensitive to movement, but not detail.

All insects have six legs

Beetles

Almost two-fifths of all insect species are beetles, with at least 300,000 different types living in every inhabitable part of the planet. They come in all shapes and sizes, but they all have tough "wing-cases" covering their delicate wings. Some, like this gold beetle, look like they are made of precious metals.

Butterflies and moths

Butterflies are unusual among insects, because they have colourful wings, with patterns formed from tiny scales that overlap like roof tiles. Moths are similar, but less colourful, because they fly by night; this eye-catching moth is an exception.

Burnet moth
flies by day

Flies

True flies have just one pair of wings, unlike most insects that have two pairs. The second pair have become "balancers" that help them fly straight and hover on the spot. Like many insects, they start life as eggs that hatch into soft-bodied larvae. These feed and grow, then turn into adults that do not grow any more.

Wasps and bees

Although notorious for their stings, most wasps use them to kill other insects to feed their young. Many live in big colonies with one breeding queen – as do many bees, which are basically vegetarian wasps.

Spiders

A spider is not an insect. Its body is built in a similar way, but it has eight legs instead of six, and no wings. Spiders are hunters and trappers, often snaring their prey in webs made of silk before killing it with a venomous bite.

Fish

The fish were the first vertebrates, or animals with backbones. They evolved more than 500 million years ago, long before there was any animal life on land. Today there are more than 27,000 species, living in fresh water as well as the oceans. They are found in all shapes and sizes, from tiny, delicate seahorses to gigantic sharks up to 20m (66ft) long.

Elongated eels

Some fish have long, sinuous, snake-like bodies. They include eels such as this freshwater eel, which swims by rippling its body in waves that drive it through the water. Freshwater eels are unusual because they swim out to sea to breed – a journey that would be deadly to most freshwater fish.

Waves push from head to tail

Sharks and rays

Unlike typical fish, sharks and rays have skeletons made of pliable, gristly cartilage. They include some of the most fearsome predators on Earth, with razor teeth and amazingly acute senses for targeting their prey – honed to perfection over some 400 million years of evolution.

Open-water fish

Most fish have bony skeletons, and sleek bodies that slip through the water easily. Many open-water fish like these tarpons use their big flank muscles and tails to propel them at high speed. A sailfish can accelerate to an astounding 100kph (62mph) – faster than all but the most powerful racing speedboats.

Colourful reef fish

Many fish live among rocks and reefs, and since they rarely have to swim fast they are not built for speed. Some have cryptic patterns and adornments that act as camouflage, concealing them from enemies. But many coral reef species such as this parrotfish are vividly coloured, like living jewels.

Flounder's right eye moves around the head

On the sea bed

In shallow seas many fish live on the sea bed. They include rays and flatfish, whose flattened bodies allow them to lie on the bottom. A flatfish actually lies on its side, but as it grows up the eye on its "bottom" side moves around its head, so both eyes are on the top side. Despite this, its mouth stays unchanged, so its face is weirdly distorted.

Deep-ocean hunters

The fish that live in the depths of the oceans inhabit a near-freezing world of permanent darkness. Many survive by hunting each other, but prey is scarce. Hunters like this viperfish have incredibly long teeth and vast, stretchy stomachs to ensure they never miss the chance of a meal.

Amphibians and reptiles

Although they look similar, amphibians and reptiles have very different lives. Amphibians such as frogs are thin-skinned animals that must stay damp, and they usually breed in water. Reptiles such as snakes have scaly skins that stop them from drying out, and many live in deserts.

Salamanders and newts

These long-tailed amphibians live in moist places, or in streams and ponds. Newts are more aquatic, and breed in water. Many salamanders do the same, migrating to ponds in the breeding season, but others lay eggs in damp ground. They are all hunters that prey on insects, worms, and other small animals.

Fire salamander can breathe through its skin

Skin produces a powerful poison

Frogs and toads

With their tail-less bodies, long hind legs, and big eyes, these amphibians are unmistakable. Many live on the ground, but others, like this tropical poison frog, hunt high in the trees. Most frogs start life as aquatic tadpoles that turn into air-breathing adults.

Scaly lizards

A lizard is a reptile, usually with four legs and a long tail – but some are legless. Scaly, waterproof skins let lizards live in dry places, but like amphibians they are cold-blooded animals that need warm weather to stay active. So most lizards, such as this Mediterranean chameleon, live in warm climates.

Long, hollow fangs inject venom

Tough, horny scales protect skin

Snakes

The slithering, legless snakes evolved from lizards and are similar in many ways. But they are more specialized for hunting, and some, like this rattlesnake, are equipped with deadly venom. Others coil around a victim so tightly that it is unable to breathe. Snakes cannot chew, so they swallow their prey whole – however big it is.

Turtles and tortoises

The massive, arching shells that protect their bodies make turtles and tortoises quite unlike other reptiles. The tortoises are famous for their slowness, but the green sea turtle is a swift swimmer.

Crocodilians

Alligators and crocodiles are powerful reptiles that hunt in the water in warmer parts of the world. Many prey mainly on fish, but the Nile crocodile seen here attacks big mammals such as antelopes and even zebras, dragging them underwater to drown.

Birds

Glamorous, colourful, and even musical, the birds are a dazzlingly successful group of animals. There are nearly 10,000 species, ranging from tiny hummingbirds to flightless giants like the ostrich. We now know that they are all feathered dinosaurs, related to the giant hunters of the distant past.

Walking tall

Although birds are famous for their flying skills, many spend more time striding about on long legs. They include storks, cranes, and birds such as herons, ibises, and these flamingos, which feed by wading through shallow water.

Hawks and owls

Many birds eat insects, but some target bigger animals such as mammals and even other birds. Hawks and eagles fly by day like most birds, but owls such as this eagle owl use their night vision and acute hearing to hunt in the dark.

Flattened bill is typical

Ducks and geese

Lakes and marshes attract flocks of waterfowl – big-bodied birds that are adapted for life on or by the water. Some have fabulous plumage, like this male mandarin duck. Others, such as swans, are among the heaviest of all flying birds.

Ocean birds

Many birds such as puffins spend most of their lives at sea, feeding on fish and other marine life. But they must return to land to breed, often nesting in big, noisy colonies on remote cliffs and islands.

Macaws are
big parrots

Iridescent blue
is caused by
scattered light

Jungle birds

Some of the most
gloriously colourful
birds live in tropical
forests, where their dramatic plumage
enhances their displays among the trees.
They include parrots, toucans, and birds
of paradise, as well as amazingly gaudy
pheasants that look almost hand-painted.

Songbirds

More than half of all bird
species are "perching
birds", or passerines.
They include songbirds
such as the Eurasian
robin, which sing to
claim territories and
deter rivals. Most of
them sing only when
breeding, but robins
also sing in winter.

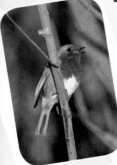

Sharp bill for
catching fish

Dense feathers
keep out cold

Flightless birds

Flight uses a lot of energy, so over
time birds that do not need to fly may
give up flying altogether. Many are fast
runners instead, like the ostrich, and
these penguins use their short wings
for swimming. But flightless birds are
vulnerable to predators, and
many are now rare.

Mammals

The animals that we feel closest to are mammals – warm, often furry creatures that feed their babies on milk. This is hardly surprising, for we are mammals too. Many mammals are small and secretive, but others are big, fast-running animals that live in herds, or powerful, quick-thinking hunters.

Carnivores

Named for their mainly meat-eating habits, the carnivores include powerful predators like this leopard, scavengers such as hyenas, and animals like bears that also eat plants. But most are fierce hunters, well equipped for catching and killing their victims.

Leopard has sharp teeth

Spots give camouflage

Primates

Humans belong to the primate group, which includes apes and monkeys such as this baboon. All primates have relatively large brains, and many live in complex societies. They mainly eat plants, but some, like chimpanzees, are also hunters.

Marine mammals

The ancestors of mammals lived on land, but some have evolved into sea creatures. They include the seals, which are superb swimmers but return to land to breed. Dolphins and whales live entirely at sea, even giving birth underwater.

Hoofed grazers

The biggest land mammals are all plant-eaters. Many are fast-running, hoofed animals like this zebra, specialized for eating grass, which is very abundant but difficult to digest. These grazers often live in herds for greater safety.

Insectivores

Many small mammals prey on insects and similar creatures. They include most of the bats, which fly by night on wings of stretched skin. They target moths in the dark by emitting high clicks and creating a sonar image from the echoes.

Rodents

Of the 4,600 known mammal species, some 2,000 are rodents, such as rats and mice, squirrels, and cavies. They all have long, chisel-like front teeth for gnawing tough plant foods, but have an amazing variety of lifestyles – living in almost every habitat from the Arctic tundra to tropical forests.

Big ears alert for danger

Red kangaroo is the biggest marsupial

Marsupials

Most mammals grow into babies inside their mothers' bodies. But marsupials such as kangaroos are born long before they are fully formed. Somehow the tiny young crawl into a pouch on the mother's belly, where they are fed on milk until they become well-developed babies.

Habitats and homes

Animals live in all kinds of places, including oceans, swamps, forests, deserts, and Arctic tundra. These places are their habitats, and animals evolve to suit them. A polar bear, for example, is very different from a brown bear, because it lives on frozen oceans rather than in forests. Within its habitat, an animal may make a special home to keep itself safe and warm, or to raise a family.

Land habitats

This gibbon lives in tropical forest, the richest land habitat. The year-round warmth means there is always plenty of food. Most other land habitats have dry or cold seasons when food is scarce. On Arctic tundra, the winters are so harsh that most animals must move away, returning in spring.

Water habitats

Life began in the oceans, and salty or fresh water is still an ideal habitat. It supports the bodies of big animals like this humpback whale, and allows many other animals to live in one spot and wait for food to drift their way.

Sand martin chicks in their burrow

Sheltered burrows

Many animals make homes by digging burrows. They are good places to hide from enemies, but more importantly their temperature stays much the same whatever the weather. This makes a burrow an excellent nursery for a young family.

Woven nests

Most birds build
nests for their eggs
and young. Some
are wonderful structures,
like this weaver bird's nest
made of woven grass
stems and suspended
from a tree. But other
birds' nests are just
scrapes in the ground,
lined with a few soft
feathers or even
nothing at all.

Snug dens

Big animals cannot dig burrows, but
they can often find cavities beneath
rocks or fallen trees that make snug
dens. For this Asiatic black bear, such
a den makes an ideal place to spend
the winter months, well insulated from
the bone-chilling temperatures outside.

A sleeping bear is safe and warm

Nest entrance is
at the bottom

Breeding colonies

Living together can make animals safer, since they
can band together to drive away enemies. Many
seabirds such as these gannets nest in big
colonies, crowded together on isolated islands
where there are no foxes to eat their eggs.

Answers

1 1c, 2a, 3b, 4b, 5d, 6d, 7d, 8c, 9c, 10a, 11a, 12d, 13b, 14c, 15a

2 1a, 2c, 3a, 4c, 5d, 6d, 7b, 8d, 9a, 10a, 11a, 12a, 13c, 14d, 15b, 16b, 17d, 18d, 19d, 20d

3 1d, 2b, 3c, 4a, 5d, 6a, 7a, 8b, 9d, 10a, 11d, 12c, 13d, 14a, 15c, 16d, 17b, 18b, 19c, 20b

4 1d, 2c, 3d, 4b, 5a, 6d, 7b, 8c, 9b, 10b, 11a, 12c, 13d, 14a, 15d

5 1a, 2c, 3d, 4d, 5c, 6a, 7b, 8a, 9a, 10c, 11d, 12c, 13c, 14a, 15a, 16c, 17a, 18c, 19b, 20a

6 1c, 2c, 3d, 4b, 5d, 6c, 7a, 8a, 9a, 10a, 11b, 12c, 13d, 14b, 15c, 16c, 17a, 18c, 19d, 20a

7 1d, 2a, 3b, 4b, 5d, 6c, 7c, 8a, 9a, 10b, 11d, 12a, 13c, 14c, 15b

8 1b, 2c, 3b, 4b, 5b, 6d, 7a, 8c, 9b, 10c, 11b, 12b, 13b, 14c, 15d, 16d, 17d, 18c, 19c, 20c

9 1a, 2a, 3c, 4b, 5a, 6b, 7d, 8b, 9c, 10d, 11d, 12a, 13b, 14b, 15c, 16a, 17d, 18b, 19c, 20a

10 1c, 2c, 3d, 4d, 5a, 6c, 7a, 8c, 9b, 10d, 11d, 12b, 13b, 14d, 15a

11 1b, 2b, 3c, 4b, 5b, 6a, 7a, 8b, 9c, 10a, 11c, 12d, 13d, 14a, 15a, 16a, 17a, 18d, 19d, 20c

12 1d, 2c, 3d, 4b, 5b, 6a, 7d, 8d, 9a, 10b, 11a, 12d, 13d, 14d, 15c, 16d, 17c, 18b, 19b, 20a

13 1d, 2b, 3c, 4a, 5c, 6c, 7a, 8c, 9a, 10b, 11b, 12d, 13b, 14a, 15d

14 1d, 2a, 3a, 4d, 5d, 6a, 7d, 8b, 9a, 10d, 11a, 12b, 13a, 14a, 15c, 16b, 17b, 18a, 19b, 20a

15 1a, 2c, 3c, 4d, 5c, 6a, 7c, 8c, 9a, 10a, 11b, 12d, 13a, 14d, 15c, 16c, 17d, 18d, 19b, 20b

16 1a, 2c, 3c, 4c, 5d, 6a, 7d, 8d, 9d, 10b, 11c, 12a, 13d, 14b, 15d

17 1d, 2a, 3c, 4c, 5d, 6d, 7c, 8d, 9c, 10c, 11c, 12c, 13c, 14b, 15c, 16c, 17c, 18c, 19d, 20a

18 1b, 2c, 3d, 4b, 5c, 6d, 7b, 8c, 9b, 10d, 11c, 12a, 13a, 14d, 15a, 16b, 17a, 18a, 19d, 20b

19 1d, 2a, 3a, 4b, 5c, 6c, 7d, 8d, 9c, 10c, 11b, 12b, 13b, 14a, 15a

20 1a, 2c, 3d, 4b, 5d, 6d, 7d, 8d, 9d, 10b, 11b, 12d, 13c, 14c, 15b, 16c, 17c, 18a, 19a, 20b

21 1c, 2b, 3b, 4a, 5b, 6b, 7d, 8b, 9a, 10c, 11c, 12c, 13a, 14c, 15a, 16c, 17c, 18b, 19d, 20a

22 1a, 2c, 3c, 4d, 5b, 6b, 7a, 8b, 9a, 10c, 11c, 12d, 13b, 14d, 15b

23 1b, 2b, 3b, 4b, 5a, 6d, 7c, 8b, 9a, 10b, 11a, 12d, 13b, 14c, 15c, 16c, 17c, 18b, 19a, 20a

24 1d, 2c, 3b, 4d, 5a, 6b, 7b, 8d, 9b, 10d, 11d, 12a, 13b, 14c, 15b, 16a, 17d, 18d, 19b, 20d

25 1a, 2d, 3d, 4d, 5c, 6a, 7a, 8a, 9c, 10c, 11b, 12c, 13b, 14b, 15d

26 1b, 2c, 3d, 4d, 5c, 6d, 7d, 8d, 9a, 10a, 11d, 12a, 13a, 14a, 15b, 16d, 17a, 18b, 19c, 20c

27 1c, 2b, 3d, 4a, 5a, 6d, 7c, 8c, 9c, 10a, 11c, 12b, 13b, 14c, 15b, 16a, 17d, 18a, 19b, 20d

28 1b, 2d, 3d, 4b, 5c, 6c, 7c, 8a, 9d, 10c, 11a, 12a, 13b, 14b, 15a

29 1b, 2a, 3d, 4c, 5d, 6a, 7d, 8d, 9c, 10a, 11c, 12a, 13a, 14d, 15c, 16a, 17c, 18a, 19b, 20c

30 1c, 2a, 3c, 4c, 5c, 6b, 7d, 8b, 9a, 10d, 11d, 12b, 13b, 14d, 15d, 16b, 17d, 18a, 19a, 20a

31 — 1c, 2a, 3c, 4d, 5c, 6a, 7b, 8b, 9a, 10b, 11b, 12c, 13d, 14c, 15a

32 — 1c, 2b, 3b, 4d, 5b, 6d, 7b, 8b, 9d, 10b, 11b, 12c, 13c, 14b, 15b, 16c, 17c, 18a, 19d, 20c

33 — 1b, 2c, 3c, 4a, 5c, 6a, 7b, 8a, 9a, 10c, 11d, 12d, 13a, 14b, 15a, 16c, 17b, 18c, 19b, 20a

34 — 1a, 2d, 3a, 4c, 5c, 6b, 7d, 8a, 9c, 10b, 11d, 12b, 13b, 14d, 15b

35 — 1c, 2c, 3c, 4a, 5b, 6a, 7d, 8a, 9b, 10a, 11b, 12d, 13a, 14b, 15c, 16a, 17d, 18b, 19b, 20c

36 — 1b, 2d, 3a, 4c, 5c, 6a, 7a, 8d, 9d, 10d, 11d, 12b, 13a, 14d, 15b, 16d, 17d, 18c, 19d, 20b

37 — 1c, 2a, 3c, 4b, 5a, 6b, 7b, 8a, 9d, 10d, 11c, 12d, 13b, 14b, 15a

38 — 1a, 2a, 3a, 4b, 5d, 6a, 7d, 8b, 9d, 10d, 11b, 12d, 13a, 14a, 15b, 16a, 17a, 18d, 19a, 20d

39 — 1b, 2c, 3a, 4b, 5d, 6c, 7b, 8c, 9a, 10a, 11a, 12d, 13d, 14a, 15a, 16d, 17c, 18a, 19d, 20c

40 — 1c, 2b, 3a, 4d, 5a, 6b, 7d, 8c, 9b, 10d, 11d, 12a, 13a, 14b, 15c

41 — 1d, 2d, 3c, 4d, 5d, 6c, 7c, 8c, 9c, 10d, 11d, 12a, 13d, 14b, 15c, 16c, 17c, 18a, 19c, 20c

42 — 1d, 2c, 3d, 4b, 5b, 6d, 7c, 8c, 9a, 10c, 11b, 12b, 13d, 14c, 15a, 16c, 17d, 18d, 19c, 20c

43 — 1b, 2c, 3b, 4b, 5b, 6b, 7c, 8b, 9a, 10d, 11a, 12d, 13c, 14a, 15a

44 — 1d, 2d, 3d, 4a, 5b, 6c, 7a, 8a, 9b, 10c, 11d, 12c, 13d, 14d, 15c, 16c, 17c, 18d, 19b, 20b

45 — 1a, 2b, 3c, 4a, 5b, 6c, 7c, 8b, 9c, 10c, 11a, 12c, 13d, 14d, 15d, 16b, 17a, 18d, 19b, 20c

46 — 1d, 2b, 3b, 4a, 5c, 6d, 7c, 8a, 9c, 10a, 11c, 12c, 13b, 14d, 15b

47 — 1d, 2d, 3a, 4c, 5a, 6a, 7d, 8c, 9d, 10b, 11b, 12b, 13b, 14c, 15c, 16c, 17a, 18b, 19c, 20c

48 — 1c, 2b, 3a, 4b, 5c, 6d, 7a, 8a, 9d, 10c, 11b, 12b, 13b, 14a, 15b, 16c, 17d, 18a, 19d, 20b

49 — 1b, 2a, 3a, 4a, 5a, 6c, 7c, 8d, 9d, 10b, 11d, 12c, 13b, 14d, 15c

50 — 1d, 2a, 3a, 4c, 5d, 6a, 7a, 8b, 9b, 10d, 11c, 12a, 13b, 14b, 15d, 16d, 17c, 18c, 19b, 20d

51 — 1a, 2b, 3a, 4d, 5b, 6a, 7b, 8c, 9d, 10c, 11b, 12a, 13a, 14a, 15b, 16c, 17a, 18a, 19c, 20a

52 — 1d, 2c, 3d, 4c, 5d, 6b, 7a, 8d, 9a, 10b, 11b, 12b, 13b, 14a, 15a

53 — 1d, 2b, 3c, 4d, 5a, 6d, 7c, 8c, 9d, 10a, 11b, 12a, 13d, 14d, 15a, 16c, 17a, 18c, 19c, 20a

54 — 1d, 2d, 3d, 4d, 5b, 6c, 7a, 8a, 9d, 10b, 11d, 12c, 13b, 14c, 15c, 16b, 17a, 18a, 19a, 20d

55 — 1d, 2c, 3a, 4b, 5c, 6c, 7c, 8a, 9b, 10c, 11d, 12a, 13d, 14a, 15b

56 — 1a, 2c, 3c, 4c, 5c, 6b, 7b, 8b, 9a, 10c, 11c, 12c, 13b, 14d, 15b, 16c, 17d, 18b, 19b, 20a

57 — 1a, 2b, 3a, 4c, 5c, 6a, 7d, 8c, 9c, 10b, 11a, 12a, 13b, 14d, 15a, 16d, 17c, 18a, 19b, 20c

58 — 1d, 2d, 3c, 4a, 5d, 6a, 7c, 8b, 9c, 10a, 11c, 12d, 13b, 14d, 15c

59 — 1a, 2b, 3b, 4a, 5a, 6a, 7a, 8b, 9c, 10d, 11d, 12a, 13a, 14d, 15d, 16c, 17b, 18c, 19d, 20b

60 — 1c, 2b, 3a, 4b, 5b, 6a, 7d, 8d, 9a, 10d, 11c, 12c, 13d, 14b, 15c, 16d, 17b, 18b, 19c, 20d

Acknowledgments

DK would like to thank: Jenny Sich for proofreading; Vibha Malhotra, James Mitchem, and Roma Malik for additional editorial work; and Sanjay Chauhan, Arup Giri, Nidhi Mehra, Namita, and Mahipal Singh for additional design work.

The publisher would like to thank the following for their kind permission to reproduce their photographs:
(Key: a – above; b – below/bottom; c – centre; f – far; l – left; r – right; t – top)

15 Dorling Kindersley: Thomas Marent (tr). **24 Corbis:** Naturfoto Honal (b). **39 Corbis:** Nigel Pavitt / JAI (bl). **48–49 Dorling Kindersley:** Barrie Watts. **54–55 Getty Images:** Tom Walker. **54 Dorling Kindersley:** Jerry Young (tl). **61 Corbis:** Tim Davis (br). **62 Dorling Kindersley:** Ian Montgomery / Birdway. com.au (tr). **U.S.F.W.S:** Dave Menke (tl). **64 NOAA:** (bl). **66 Dorling Kindersley:** Lindsey Stock (bl). **70 Dorling Kindersley:** Ted Benton (bc). **76 Dorling Kindersley:** Thomas Marent (tr). **78–79 Getty Images:** Life On White. **85 Dorling Kindersley:** Thomas Marent (tr). **90–91 Alamy Images:** Juniors Bildarchiv. **96 Dorling Kindersley:** Ted Benton (cb). **96–97 Dorling Kindersley:** Jamie Marshall. **104 Corbis:** Ron & Valerie Taylor / Steve Parish Publishing (bl). **108 Corbis:** Momatiuk – Eastcott (t). **109 Dorling Kindersley:** Thomas Marent (cl). **U.S. Geological Survey:** Tania Larson (tr). **114–115 Corbis:** Fritz Polking / Frank Lane Picture Agency. **119 Dreamstime.com:** Matthewgsimpson (br). **125 Corbis:** Denis Scott (tr). **126 Dreamstime.com:** Lynn Bystrom (br). **127 Corbis:** Tom Brakefield (tr). **131 Dorling Kindersley:** Ted Benton (br). **133 Corbis:** Jeffrey L. Rotman (clb); David Wrobel / Visuals Unlimited (br). **135 Dorling Kindersley:** Jerry Young (cr). **NOAA:** Dr. Robert Schroeder (br). **136 Dorling Kindersley:** Sean Hunter Photography (br). **137 Dorling Kindersley:** Kim Taylor (cl). **138 Dorling Kindersley:** Philip Dowell (c). **NOAA:** (br). **140 Dorling Kindersley:** Thomas Marent (tr). **NOAA:** Stan Butler (cl)

Jacket images: Front: **Getty Images:** GK Hart / Vikki Hart

All other images © Dorling Kindersley
For further information see: **www.dkimages.com**